Hope Survives

Strength After A Traumatic Brain Injury

7/30/18

Megan Loiaconi Hurley

Dear Jeannie,

You always see forward,
You always build up
and never take 'no' for
an answer. Your resilient
strength has lifted me
up at more times then
you know. I can't
think of a better way
to define Hope.
Peace, Love, Zumba,
megan

For special discounts on bulk purchases,
please email Sales@KastPublishing.com.

Cover and back photo credits: Karla Trujillo.
Zumba® is trademark of Zumba Fitness, LLC. Used under license.

ISBN: 978-0-9962097-4-8

Printed in the United States of America.

Hope Survives

Strength After A Traumatic Brain Injury

Kast Publishing, LLC

Dedicated to my parents, Nancy Loiaconi, and in memory of my father, Stephen Loiaconi.

Mom, thank you for being by my side, holding my hand, and lifting me up throughout my healing journey. Dad, I know you are always with me and watching over me. You both inspire and strengthen me.

Acknowledgments

I would like to express my gratitude to the many people who saw me through this book and who made the dream of creating this book a reality.

I am especially grateful to my husband, Bob Hurley, for his strength, inspiration, love and patience. Bob stayed awake every night with me until I typed my daily word count goal, told me that he was proud of me every morning and night and constantly said that he had faith in me. Bob is the reason that I went to sleep each night believing this book would come true. I love you so much more.

I especially thank my mom, brother and husband for collectively piecing the parts of my story together. Their courage to open a healed wound from which they've protected me during these years gave me a second chance to start a new life with endless possibilities.

I would like to express my sincere thanks and love to the many family members and dear friends who comforted and encouraged me on this journey through ongoing recovery; my champions. I especially hold in my heart and remember those who are no longer with me, but never had a doubt I would overcome and never gave up on me; my lighthouses.

I offer special thanks to my dear friend Kelly Tobey, who made sure I didn't quit before I put my pen to paper. She gave me a notebook with the New York City skyline across the cover and said, "Start writing. You have a bigger story to tell." Kelly is a sounding board and a loyal source of encouragement and guidance, and she stands by my side for brain injury advocacy.

I am particularly thankful to photographer and friend, Karla Trujillo. I am honored for her photography to be a part of this book. The cover photo welcomes the reader to walk on this journey with me. Karla's interpretation of my journey and honesty breathed fresh air into the text. Her pictures capture the intensity of the pages to come and a hopeful future.

I greatly appreciate the time and honest feedback of friend, Andrew Murphy, who selflessly offered his support, had impromptu brainstorm sessions, read pages a few at a time and suggested comments. His thorough feedback allowed me to re-examine every word, sentence, and topic through a different point of view; resulting in more in-depth writing.

My grateful thanks are extended to Sherry Kast of Kast Publishing, LLC. Sherry saw the inspiration of hope in my story during our first phone call in December 2017. She is a true role model of professionalism, compassion and courage to take on this project from the start and never look back. Sherry is a talented mentor, writing coach, editor, publisher, support system and friend.

Foreward

I met Megan Hurley through the Project Athena Foundation, an incredible organization dedicated to helping women who have experienced a tragedy, go from survivor to adventure athlete. We both fell in love with this organization for very different reasons. Megan had suffered a traumatic brain injury and during her recovery, she discovered the Project Athena Foundation. The nonprofit helped Megan with her physical comeback by sponsoring her to become a certified U-Jam Fitness® instructor.

On the other hand, I supported the Project Athena Foundation by fundraising for an adventure to hike the Grand Canyon from rim to rim. That experience changed my life and introduced me to some incredible women who faced extreme difficulties and fought fervently to overcome those challenges. Megan is one such fighter.

We are both in the Project Athena Foundation Facebook group. Megan was seeking a publisher and asked for a recommendation on the social platform. A friend in the same group recommended me and I was the fortunate one chosen to help Megan.

My role with Megan's book was different than any other book I have written or published. I took on the role of writing coach. Megan wanted intensely to write about her journey; it was going to be part of her mental comeback. However, she needed help with structure and focus.

She worked diligently, writing day after day to piece together a story of healing and hope in which she could not remember details following a tragic fall that led to her brain injury.

Every two weeks, I held coaching calls with Megan. She created an outline and I developed a schedule to keep her focused and organized. I could hear the anxiety in her voice during our first few calls. I knew she was wondering if she could complete this monumental task much less write a chapter.

With meticulous notes and a willingness to pour her heart and soul into this project, Megan deemed that writing a book would be part of her mental comeback. She has inspired me with her tenacity and her spirit for helping others while increasing awareness of traumatic brain injuries. I hope you enjoy her journey of strength and resilience as much as I did, witnessing it first-hand as her writing coach.

Sherry Kast

Preface

This is a story of hope, change and choices. One of choosing optimism in what can feel like a world of despair. It is about the fear of losing one's personal self and the prospect of gaining a new self-assured identity. This is a story about second chances.

The intent of sharing my journey is to help people overcome what can seem impossible, and believe that choosing hope is an option, no matter how far away, painful or unrealistic it may be. Penning my story marks ten years since I fell in a library, resulting in a traumatic brain injury (TBI), an alteration in brain function caused by an external force.[1] That one moment on July 10, 2008, changed everything in my life forever, and it opened my eyes to a world I never had the courage to dip my toe into, let alone dive headfirst.

The world in which I live now is different from the one before my accident, and it brings many unknowns. My personal and professional life is not the same and will never be the same as it was previously. I now accept that, but it leaves me to answer the question of what do I do when my life and dreams are out of my control? Do I give up or find new dreams? I do know that I want to leave a testimony of my accident, ongoing recovery and comeback journey since 2008 with a message of inspiration, even when inspiration can be hard to come by.

Though told from a traumatic brain injury survivor, this book is not only for people affected by brain injuries. Compassion and fellowship unite us in the face of crisis in more ways than we may realize. At different points in our lives, we have experienced strength; we have felt scared or alone; we have been in pain; we have helped someone; we have been sick; we have been a hero; we have put our lives in the hands of a doctor; we have reached a goal; we have dealt with money issues or lost a job; and none of us want to believe the only resolution is darkness.

Hope is a choice for us to make, but we do not need to go on our journey alone. For me, it's not just finding hope through the despair of living with my TBI, even though this project started out that way. The more time I spent unpacking that concept and the choices I have made during the past decade throughout the cycle of hope versus despair, I realized how much I have grown beyond the TBI. Now I can look at life, and what comes my way, with optimism.

What continues to humble me again and again, is the extreme effort and resilience with which the body will fight. Year after year, and test after test, doctors told me results, updates, and courses of action that were grim to say the least. I still remind myself that my body fought to stay alive, and that it is still determined to keep fighting.

Adjusting away from the past and out of our comfort zones, the unfamiliar can be overwhelming; but we can't live in the before. Life pushes us ahead; forward to the next chapter. We have the choice to stare backward at our lives before, or open our eyes to everything after, which is new to explore.

Ten years later, I sit here, piecing events together, trying to build ten days of memories that never formed in my brain, and never will. I want to share every step of my journey—the pain and healing—from my heart. The one challenge is that I am telling a story that starts with ten days I don't remember, and the following weeks that are hazy.

Since 2008, my husband, Bob Hurley, my mom, Nancy Loiaconi, and my brother, Stephen Loiaconi, have told me portions about that life-altering fall and hospitalization. Not until I asked each of them one-on-one at the start of this project did they truly go back to 2008, recalling every painstaking detail. In three separate conversations, we unearthed all of the horrific details minute by minute, up until the point that I started to remember.

These talks were both emotional and clinical. Silence. Facts. Pain. Hope. Fear. Unknown.

I'm not afraid to open this nightmare from so long ago because I don't remember living through any of it. Each family member packed that tragic summer day away, never planning to relive every minute. Then there are other parts of this horror movie they will never see; but are vivid for me and still keep me up at night after ten years.

When I asked Bob to sit with me and walk me though these days, he said, "Of course, but I'm sure your mom will be able to tell you more than I can."

When I asked my mom the same question, she said, "Of course, but I'm sure Bob will be able to tell you more than I can."

Stephen's response to my request was, "Sure we can talk, but 2008 was a long time ago and I don't think I remember a lot."

They each underestimated their contributions to my story. Everyone added missing pieces the others didn't have. I desperately needed them to put this entire puzzle together. Each of them walked into the same crisis at different points on the timeline, observing me unresponsive in the same hospital and recovering in my own home through their own perspectives. I feel comforted knowing that I was never alone, and that we can create my new story together as a family, away from the fear.

Every TBI is different, making every recovery different. One commonality among survivors is the determination to bring the awareness and education of this topic to the forefront as the discussion is not prevalent. TBI recovery, including physical, mental, emotional and intellectual deficits, and rehabilitation, can be lifelong for some. The numerous doctor appointments, prescriptions, and looks of misfortune from strangers do not reflect the inner resilience and compassion we possess as survivors.

This accident wasn't the worst experience that happened to me, but it was the experience that changed me the most. I want to leave a legacy, not just leave. For those facing challenges, know that hope survives.

Disclaimer

Please note, *"Hope Survives: Strength After A Traumatic Brain Injury"* is told from the experience of one traumatic brain injury survivor, not a medical professional or expert. No attempt or intention is made to offend or dismiss other survivors, caregivers, or loved ones who have lost their battles with brain injuries.

Chapter 1
July 2008 Fall

My mom helped me wash the dried blood and EEG glue out of my hair while I sat on my new shower chair that I would have to use from now on to keep me from falling. This ten-day-old crusty mess of the sticky glue used to secure the eighteen electrodes to my skull ran down my face mixing with tears of fear and pain, along with the confusion of where I was and the insecurity of the unknown ahead. I just came home from a week-and-a-half hospital stay of which I had no memory. I will never remember the moment that skewed the course of my life forever. I remember walking into a library in 2008 and am told that I was swept away in an ambulance.

Early in the day on July 10, 2008, my husband, Bob, and I dropped my mom at the airport to catch her flight home to New York after a two-week visit with us in California. We rushed home so I could drop off Bob and head up the highway to research books with a friend for my graduate school class. My friend later told me that shortly after combing the stacks of books at the local library I cried out a stream of incoherent words, clutched the wall and had what would be later diagnosed as my first grand mal seizure.

The Mayo Clinic defines a grand mal seizure, also known as a generalized tonic-clonic seizure, as a loss of consciousness and violent muscle contractions. It is caused by abnormal electrical activity throughout the brain.[2]

To this day, after tireless testing, my doctors still don't know what caused that seizure. Right away, the convulsing dropped me to the ground. I fell backward, and my head hit the marble floor, fracturing my skull.

The librarian quickly dialed 911 while my friend called Bob to meet us at the hospital. The ambulance delivered me directly to the emergency room (ER) around 2:00 p.m.

I waited to be seen in the emergency room; where I was observed and scrutinized at my most vulnerable when my body couldn't even function without assistance. What a horrifying feeling. The ER is filled with great irony. Probably the greatest of all is that most people are in such serious condition that they don't remember the life-changing visit which is forever burned into everyone else's minds. You only can enter by the fact that your body is in the most dangerous condition possible. Those of us who are lucky to live are saved by doctors we will never see after being transferred to the intensive care unit (ICU). It is the oddest relationship I can think of to cultivate such a high level of intimacy, and then vanish from each other's lives just as quickly.

Bob arrived just a few minutes after the ambulance. He wouldn't be allowed to see me until I was steady in the surgical intensive care unit (SICU). Doctors worked diligently to stabilize me.

I was diagnosed as status epilepticus (SE). SE is any seizure that lasts more than five minutes.[3] Mine lasted hours. After six hours, the seizures persisted, not responding to medication. At that point, I required more aggressive management with Propofol sedation and intubation. According to the Brain Injury Association of America, the Glasgow Coma Scale (GCS) is how a treatment team evaluates a person's level of consciousness (LOC) and the severity of brain injury by attempting to elicit body movements (M), opening of the eyes (E), and verbal responses (V).[4]

The GCS ranges from a three, deep unconsciousness, to a fifteen, being fully awake. During the ride to the hospital, I went into a coma while seizing. I was admitted to the hospital in a coma on the lowest GCS level. I had a total score of three—no motor response, no eye opening, and no verbal response. I was at the worst place and still alive. While being treated, I slipped out of the coma and the seizing continued. The doctors needed to intubate me and induce me back into a coma.

After calling my mom and brother, Bob left messages for my other doctors to apprise them of the emergency. He paced anxiously in the waiting room until 8:00 p.m. when he finally passed the SICU gatekeepers to hold my hand. The first time he saw me I was on a ventilator, in restraints which is common practice for seizure patients, and had a cervical collar around my neck to prevent injury to the spinal cord by immobilizing a potentially unstable spine.[5]

On top of the piles of paperwork Bob was asked to fill out, extra confusion came up because nobody had my insurance information upon admittance to the ER, which did not help bring any calm to the crisis.

I had packed my purse and wallet so quickly that day and it was the only day that I ever left the house without my insurance card.

My mother turned on her cell phone as she stepped off the airplane at 9:00 p.m. at the John F. Kennedy International Airport. She was tired from her long flight across the county back to New York and couldn't wait to get home and into her bed for a long, relaxing night of sleep. She looked down at her phone to see a missed call and voicemail from Bob. She knew right away that something was wrong; she could feel it.

Standing in the terminal with her suitcase and jacket, she listened to Bob's message, "Megan had an accident and is in a coma."

There were no flights back to the West Coast that night. She couldn't be at my side until the next day. Her relaxing evening disappeared. Her time to sleep never started. As soon as she ran into her house, she opened her computer to book a flight to San Diego, leaving seven hours later.

Adrenaline took over as she hurriedly tossed through her closet to grab any mix of clothes to swap out for the suitcase she just brought home.

When mom's early morning flight landed in San Diego, Bob's mom greeted her at the airport and they drove directly to the hospital where Bob was waiting with me.

The neurologist pulled him aside that morning informing him of possible debilitating outcomes and of the 28% mortality rate associated with the accident I sustained. The neurologist noted, however, that most people who undergo a fall of this nature are quite elderly and are not typically in as good of shape to recover.[6]

The neurologist stopped at my room to check my status and update my family daily. He explained that I would stay in the SICU for continued monitoring of the swelling in my brain. If it didn't go down soon enough, the neurosurgeon would need to drill into my skull to relieve the pressure on my brain. While incapacitated, I wore compression cuffs around my legs that inflated and relaxed continuously to prevent blood clots by keeping blood flowing.[7] Learning about all of this later made the experience sound quite clinical, which is where I started losing my personal identity right from the start. I became a patient.

My mom kept watch over me all the time, holding her Kindle in hand, but never taking a break to read anything on it. She wanted to provide comfort, care, and take away my pain at the same time. She watched me meticulously for any change in my condition or any detail a nurse or doctor might have missed while they blinked. As she watched me, she noticed that while I lay in a coma, perfectly still and straight, my arms were moving up and down, very slowly and slightly. A nurse explained to her that even though my arms were only going up and down two to three inches at a time, that movement was still seizure activity while I was in a coma.

After being on the respirator and in the coma for three days, the doctor took me off the ventilator sooner than planned. Bob and my mom weren't with me. However, it was the right time to take out the breathing tube, medically, because my body was starting to wake up, and the doctors didn't want me to wake up and be alert on the respirator. Once I became conscious, the game plan changed.

Without needing a respirator, I was transferred down to the critical care step down unit.

Here, the same neurosurgeon and neurologists followed my case closely, and there were always two nurses stationed outside my room constantly monitoring me and my roommate. The woman with whom I shared the room was quite elderly and didn't stay very long.

The doctors ran tests on me every day. I had so many MRIs, CTs, and X-Rays, more than my mom and Bob can even recall. The hospital priest visited me a few times to pray with my family. I do not recall these visits, but I still have the rosary beads to this day that he blessed and gave to Bob at my bedside.

Bob wanted to do everything to save me and take this nightmare away from me. The nurses wouldn't let him sleep on the plastic chairs in my room overnight per hospital policy. The nurses encouraged everyone to talk with me because they didn't know exactly what I could hear or absorb.

Bob brought my favorite book, *The Great Gatsby*, by F. Scott Fitzgerald, and held my hand while reading aloud to me. He later told me that he only read through the first eight to ten pages before I woke up. He was thrilled because he can't stand that book. Bob just wanted me to be happy and bring me something from home that might comfort me.

My family only left the room or let go of my hand when the doctors arrived to run tests. Their required exits often sent them to the hospital cafeteria for forty-minute stints. They didn't like being away from me for any longer when I was in such critical condition. My mom, Bob, and brother, Stephen, all say that the cafeteria food was great, and they loved the coffee.

Visiting hours were from 8:00 a.m. to 11:00 p.m. My family stationed themselves in my room for every second of those fifteen hours, and when they needed to leave the room, the nurses took over patrol to watch me closely as to not miss any first signs of hope that I would show.

This was especially important during the days when the coma wore down and I slowly became lucid, as my eye, motor, and verbal responses would start indicating the severity of lasting aftereffects from the brain swelling.

Preparing for these possibilities were not the outcomes that brought hope to my family, even though they were realities. The first few days were inconsistent in terms of my showing any responses to movement, eye-opening, and verbal communication. Again, the doctors could not predict exactly to what extent the swelling on my brain would cause specific deficits until I woke up and tried moving and talking.

After I was out of the coma and breathing on my own, I was still very weak and only slightly responsive. The first stage I tried to take was eye-movement. My mom and the nurses could see that I was trying to open my eyes, but the muscles weren't strong enough, and I needed another day to try again. When I finally opened my eyes, I wasn't able to see anything. I was awake and kept looking around with my open eyes, seeing nothing after all this time. My mom, Bob, and the doctors were concerned this meant that I would be permanently blind.

The next events brought new concerns, but a tiny bit of hope. I had the strength to open my eyes again, and this time I could slightly see, which was a huge relief to everyone, myself most of all.

Then, I had my first verbal response, but not a strong one. I started to utter sounds, but not words from my lips. I did this off and on for a lengthy time, while opening and closing my eyes, but I still was not able to form words. Now the concern was elevated to the point that I wouldn't be able to talk anymore. I would either need to re-learn how to speak or never regain that skill.

Finally, I turned a small corner which brought another glimmer of hope when I think everyone really needed it most. I went back to keeping my eyes closed, but in a soft voice, I clearly said that, "I have the desire to be satiated." At that point, when the doctors heard me, they were satisfied that I had not lost the ability to speak.

I was told later that I kept thanking everyone and was very polite in my semi-conscious state of pain. Bob kept track of the names of each nurse at every shift and my mom kept names of each doctor. Between the two of them, no detail would go unnoticed.

My circulation was healthy because of the work from the compression sleeves on my legs. But something still wasn't right. I hadn't shown any muscle movement other than my eyes and the slight talking.

Finally, I was awake and speaking in a louder tone. With my eyes closed again, I asked my mom if she had met my nurse and if I offered my nurse something to eat or drink. The nursing staff kept telling Bob and my mom how polite I was.

With these steps forward, our insurance insisted on transferring me to a different hospital. The hospital where I was admitted was not within my insurance system, but it was the closest trauma center to my accident site.

The policy was that I be brought to the closest treatment facility, no matter what insurance system, and then transfer me to a hospital within my network when I was physically up to the standard of care they could provide to meet my medical needs.

After a total of nine days receiving excellent care from a near-fatal accident, I was transferred quickly during a weekend for insurance billing purposes. They insisted I be evaluated by a doctor in my insurance system before safely discharging me home. This was not the case at all. The ambulance arrived to transfer me between hospitals on a Saturday afternoon. I was admitted to the hospital in my insurance network and put in a room for one night. I saw a doctor once, who was not even in my system. He was covering for another doctor who was supposed to be on-call for the weekend. He evaluated me and sent me home.

Chapter 2
2008 Transition Home

I was in extremely bad shape when I got home. I had non-stop migraines, experienced horrible dizziness, and slept around the clock. Bob and my mom were afraid that I was slipping back into a coma since I slept for twenty-two hours straight after coming home. Bob called 911 and we went back to the hospital from where I had just been discharged and was once again admitted.

However, there were no beds in the step-down unit. I stayed on a gurney in the hallway being moved to open spaces as they became available for a few minutes at a time. My headache was so severe that the pounding in my head would not stop. The fluorescent lights above in the hallway amplified what felt like a sword fight in my skull. I begged and begged the doctor for any type of pain pill for migraines, but he wouldn't administer anything until I was settled into a room.

The cycle of despair versus hope reared its ugly head and I was powerless, lying there in the hallway. The only choice I made was to curl into a ball in the fetal position, cover my entire body, including my head, with the paper-thin hospital sheet, and cry.

I was finally admitted to a room, given pain medicine and a hospital meal, and then left alone until the next morning when a doctor I had never seen before walked into the room, signed my discharge papers, and left.

When we got home, Bob and my mom walked my weak, unbalanced, and emaciated body into the bedroom.

None of us knew what to expect. In the middle of the first night, I got dizzy and fell out of bed, hitting my head on the nightstand. I didn't realize what happened. Bob was so worried he surrounded the bed with pillows. We had no idea what the next day held in store, let alone the next ten years.

This transition home was an unsettling experience, since Bob and I had only been living in San Diego for exactly two years and two weeks when I fell. San Diego was home for us by then, but neither of us, thankfully, had gone through a crisis that required us to communicate with the people in our lives in New York and Connecticut, where we grew up.

My mom and Bob did the hard work of notifying relatives on both sides of the family and very close friends in San Diego and New York. Since it was so early on, there wasn't much news to pass along other than I had an accident, fell, was in a coma, did not need brain surgery, was home safely, and nobody knew yet what the long-term deficits were going to be.

They don't give you a TBI manual when being released from the hospital. There is no standard operating procedure of what to expect. My husband and I had to learn as much as possible on our own about a TBI, as well as how to care for someone with a TBI at home.

Everything in life changed immediately. At first, there were many physical and occupational transitions at home. Bob and my mom moved toiletries and nightstand items near me, so I could reach them a little easier. They put pillows around me, so I wouldn't fall out of bed again. The hospital sent me home with so many prescriptions for anti-seizure, pain control, migraines and at least three more, all of which I needed to take at different times of day.

Bob made a color-coded chart for each pill with the dose and what time of day I needed to take my medicine. We taped the regiment to the mirror for the first month home. He also called the academic dean where I was in graduate school to explain what happened and that I needed to put my degree on hold for a while. He was wonderful—he had the strength and patience to do everything I couldn't.

After about two weeks, I wanted to speak with my family and friends, but only had the strength and stamina to hold the phone up for two minutes maximum. I made a list of who I wanted to call and spaced out time accordingly throughout the day, so I had enough breaks for rest in between calls. I missed everyone so much. I felt empty trying to heal without my world of familiarity encompassing me.

Two years hadn't been long enough for Bob and me to create a full life on the other side of the country. The calls were so impersonal; trying to explain to those closest in my life about something so traumatic over a phone.

I couldn't answer any questions because I didn't remember the accident. Then I couldn't talk any longer, so I needed to cut these most painful conversations short.

To me, I was hanging up on family. My life in New York was not just a name and address. The longtime friends who I hold so closely are part of me and my family. We have been there for each other through the various stages of our lives, even if we weren't in the same place. My parents are second parents to my friends, and I know I have many loving parents around the country.

It's an odd feeling to have an entire life across the country in New York with family and friends who are not be able to physically cross paths with my life in San Diego on a daily basis. While everyone was easy to reach with a phone call or text message, technology did not and still does not allow for sharing vulnerability or hugs.

However, it was a blessing to be able to connect with my close friends and family throughout this ordeal.

Suffering from a TBI means not knowing how to find my identity again, literally and figuratively. My former identity doesn't exist anymore, and I live in a 'new normal.' I remember asking my doctor when I got to go home in 2008 when I would feel normal again. He told me that I wouldn't ever feel the same because my old life doesn't exist anymore.

Now, I live in a 'new normal' that I can choose to thrive in or not. I am very lucky that my outcome was not more severe from this accident. I do have deficits, including short-term memory loss. It's okay with me that I don't remember what I ate for breakfast or what day it is. I remember my wedding day. I remember my childhood with my father before he passed away when I was twenty-two.

After two months, the long-term unforeseen changes slowly became permanent fixtures in my life that I constantly make adjustments for today. I still don't have the energy to be active for more than two to three hours each day. The brain injury caused ataxia, a lack of muscle control or coordination of voluntary movements that can occur from damage to the brain or spinal cord from a blow to head.[8] This accounts for struggling with my balance, maintaining my core steadiness, walking in a straight line, and staying aligned when stretching.

Some of these deficits have improved with hard work throughout the years, but there are times when I still notice the decreased control of my fine motor skills, including when I can't thread a needle, fit my key in the front door or apply eyeliner. There are times that I can't stand up from a chair without wobbling or being unsteady on my feet. I reach out for the wall, a chair, or a person with a look of horror on my face while I try not to fall from standing with both feet planted on the ground.

In addition to ataxia, I struggle with double vision, which poses serious limitations. My experience with double vision is frustrating because there is no consistency or specific trigger for when it starts. From out of nowhere, whether I'm wearing glasses or contacts, everything around me doubles and I can't maintain my orientation or stability. I need to stop what I'm doing, sit down, and get a ride home immediately.

Not knowing when I might experience double vision makes walking around unsafe for me, and the fear and insecurity raises my anxiety levels. My energy level drops for the rest of the day. Periodically, I get these episodes for which I never needed to accommodate in my old normal.

Along with other immediate changes, a lot of independence slips away after coming home with a TBI. The California Department of Motor Vehicles (DMV) sent a letter suspending my driver's license until a neurologist observes that I legally meet the criteria to drive again by not having any seizure activity for one year due to 'loss of consciousness.' I also can't safely swim, rollerblade, or ice skate. At first, this was not a big deal. I had so much paperwork to respond to, fill out, file and review, as well as invoices to pay upon my return that the letter from the DMV did not stand out as anything specific. I was also too weak to even think about driving anyplace. All I wanted, and physically could do, was to go to bed. I wasn't looking ahead to when I would feel the void of that independence being ripped away.

I can't describe any of the grand mal seizures I've experienced, as I lose consciousness and black out for the twenty seconds to two minutes they take place. Witnesses tell me I've had typical tonic-clonic grand mal seizures consisting of initial violent muscle contractions followed by arms and legs jerking rapidly, concluding with my lips and face turning blue from lack of oxygen to my brain.[9]

When I regain consciousness after the seizure, I tend to be unaware of the event and physically exhausted because of the extreme muscle contractions and need for oxygen. My anxiety levels heighten because my body experienced something wrong, but my mind is too disoriented to place the sequence of events. Fortunately for me, I do not experience grand mal seizures frequently, about once every six months to a year. This is good because it means my treatment plan is moving in the right direction.

Other adjustments come with a new seizure disorder. In addition to grand mal seizures, I experience focal seizures regularly. Focal seizures result from abnormal electrical activity in one area of the brain causing involuntary jerking of a body part, such as an arm or leg.[10] Currently, I have a focal seizure every three days that lasts between fifteen seconds to two minutes. For the past ten years, the muscles in both or either arms and both or either legs spontaneously spasm and twitch.

Unfortunately, I do not feel a warning before one of the focal seizures begins, but since I am conscious; I just guide myself to the floor or a chair. These focal seizures are much less frequent and less severe now. For the first few years following my fall, I would have up to seven each day, all of which exerted the most violent wrenching and jolting in all four of my limbs. This improvement is just one example of how I am able to keep looking up through the tunnel, and stay hopeful that all of the medication, testing, and setbacks will be worth the wait.

Chapter 3
Forever A Teacher

Accepting that my life exists in a 'new normal' is hard because I remember my 'old normal.' I actually went through a grieving process on the loss of my former professional life, one that I will not return to again.

I was an English teacher. Composition and communication came easy for me. I now struggle with communication and need an hour to put three sentences together. Forming thoughts into sentences that make sense together is so frustrating and draining, and actually hurts. It makes me not feel smart anymore. I can't always spell correctly and fifty percent of the time I can't verbally express what I am trying to say. I've actually lost a few friends over not being able to communicate clearly. I am also grateful for the true friends who have stayed by my side for ten years and have more patience than I can imagine.

I don't like to look over my shoulder at my past because I miss so much of it. In fact, I am no longer capable of looking back at my life due to lack of cognition.[11] I still have the books on my shelves that I once taught from, gathering dust, questioning if they will ever be opened again. Teaching wasn't even the way I entered the working arena after college, but it was the path I ultimately chose and loved.

It's one thing to think about not having control in a life or death situation versus actually not having control. This was the first time that I didn't, and still don't have, control of the direction of my professional life. Fortunately, there are foundations and support groups available to help me, as well as other survivors.

My mom always said that my resume read like I was thirty years older than I am because I listed so many different skills and experiences, either working two jobs at one time or having three different titles with various departments at school. I started taking graduate classes while working full time. I was armed with a foundation to be a successful communicator, which proved to be invaluable transitioning through different fields until I found the right fit for me.

My first job was in public relations and then marketing. Later, I found my passion in education as a high school counselor and teacher. The classroom is where I flourished as the smart kid while giving to others the whole time. I haven't taught in a school in ten years and I'm accepting that I will probably never return to teaching English literature or writing.

Teaching English literature and writing felt like winning a prize every day. When I walked through the school gates at an all-girls private school, I wasn't at work for me; I was at work for my students. When they walked into my classroom each day, it was our time.

School is a society with an automatic need to have rules and function within specific parameters. I never understood this need or saw eye-to-eye with it. I saw school as a space for my students to grow and learn first, but there were times I questioned the value of these rules when they would hold back teachable moments. That didn't make my classroom the easy one, instead it was the opposite.

I was definitely one of the whacky English teachers most people have in high school, and I knew it. I taught ninth, tenth and eleventh graders, which gave me a lot of material to be creative in class.

I remember the teachers who challenged me, opened my mind and inspired me to teach, and I modeled my class after the lessons that forced me to think critically. When I taught, I prepared diligently for my lesson plans. I made notes that I left on my desk during class to be sure I didn't leave anything out.

I practiced for my classes in front of a mirror every night down to the minute in each class block. I factored in the amount of time I felt was needed for students to respond to questions. I was never nervous with my students. I made a commitment that my students were going to learn—actively and analytically.

Back to School Night was usually held two weeks into the school year when parents spent the evening visiting their child's classes and meeting their teachers for the year. For teachers, it's like speed-dating. Every fifteen minutes, I would showcase the upcoming year's books, tests, major projects, and grading scale, as well as hold a question and answer period for thirty parents at a time before switching to a new group. My opening monologue started with, "Welcome, I'm very excited to be your daughter's English teacher this year. She will probably hate this class and you probably won't know if she is telling you the truth." Every face in the room nodded with a look of refreshing honesty. "Give me another week."

Then the parents became intrigued.

"I will be the teacher who will challenge them, make them work harder than before, and participate every day. In about a month, they will come home with an ah-ha moment and realize they are learning."

To the ninth-grade parents, I stomped the *Odyssey* on the desk and would say, "They will read this 800-page poem in January and have a blast."

To the tenth-grade parents, I promised them their daughters will start a conversation about *Othello* in November so they might want to read up on this classic.

I would bow to the junior parents and tell them that their kids will have a tough year ahead with me, but they will not forget it. "They will read the dark and transcendent of American Literature that gives them a chance to discover their own voice in a way like never before." I also informed the parents I would bring my experience as a college counselor and devote a unit to writing college essays in the springtime.

Sometimes parents would ask the question, "Can I tell her what's going to happen this year or is it a surprise?" I usually advised, "Let her tough out the first month and find her ah-ha moment on her own."

The school year gets a little more fun when the students walk into class wondering why their parents are no longer on their side about "the mean English teacher who is hard on them."

I always arranged my classroom in two rows of half-moons with an opening for me to walk around throughout the whole period—there was no 'back of the room' in which to hide. There was no texting or doing homework for another class. I wanted to be the teacher who made them love learning and critical thinking.

I knew it would take a while; I just needed them to trust me on the journey. I wanted them to understand that the classroom was theirs and that they needed to make it a comfortable place to learn. They thought it was a trick, but I was laying the foundation for them to carve out their individuality through literature and writing.

The first thing I did every year was tell the students, "Sit anywhere—no assigned seats."

So many blank stares back at me, like a deer in the woods.

"How do we know where to sit?" they'd ask, "Where do we go?"

To end this madness, I explained, "You can sit wherever you want to. You can change your seat every day or sit on the floor. All I care about is that you are physically in the room. I don't believe you will learn better from any one desk compared to another. If you think you will learn better in another seat, then get up and move."

I just needed them to sit down and open their minds. I knew it wouldn't be easy and they didn't trust me, but that it would be worth it when they did.

I could tell when everything fell in place when the tenth graders debated about *Othello* throughout their entire lunch period or when they came into my room after school to just talk about the book like a soap opera. The ninth graders walked into class with their copies of the *Odyssey* nearly falling apart, some held together by rubber bands, shouting out questions about what they read the night before plus three of the next nights non-stop.

"Why did Penelope stay married to Odysseus?" "She was a desperate housewife!" "What was the plan if his father died?" "If Odysseus was so smart, why couldn't he just get home?" "Why didn't the queen fire the maids?"

My students needed to have notebooks and a pen with them in class. Students in all class sections from all grade levels walked into the room, sat down, opened their notebooks, and looked at the whiteboard for their daily warm-up writing assignment. The first two minutes of each class were dedicated to the students focusing their minds and exercising their voices on paper. The warm-up question was never very deep or challenging, just something to get started writing.

The warm-up assignment usually related to the prior night's reading assignment in some small way. At the end of the two minutes, everyone in class needed to share at least one sentence aloud. The point of the warm up was to generate ideas, responses, and discussion of each other's comments and ultimately have at least one student relate some aspect of the conversation to our subject matter. I mediated the discussion flow, but the mature, rich ideas and connections were all coming from the students just a few minutes into class.

My classroom became a space for the students, and I created the setting of our current reading inside the room. When the eleventh graders read, *The Scarlet Letter*, by Nathaniel Hawthorne, students built models of the scaffold that we placed around the room. When they read, *The Yellow Wallpaper*, by Charlotte Perkins Gilman, I would wallpaper the entire room with plastic yellow table clothes. In reading *Romeo and Juliet*, the freshmen created love letters between the two young lovers, plus letters between other characters in the play.

This activity helped the students understand the minds of the characters. When the juniors started *The Great Gatsby*, I dressed in a full pink flapper dress with a feather headdress and beaded jewelry and played the Charleston as they walked into the room on the first day. The setting and culture are such crucial parts of the novel that I wanted them immersed in the book from the start.

I pushed my students to work hard and learn critical thinking and analysis. Without those skills, they wouldn't develop any interest in learning. So, I pushed them and pushed them to become lifelong learners, always asking questions. The most different and thought-provoking way that I led class was by turning the discussion over to the students. I was afraid they would lose interest in all of the dimensions literature holds if they just walked into class and I told them what the readings meant. The two rules in class were that everyone needed to participate, and nobody's answer was wrong. There are many ways to interpret literature and I didn't want anyone to feel disrespected or that their participation was invalid. I also told them to take notes throughout class on anything that came up. If it was said in the classroom, it was fair game to be on a test.

I loved watching their minds run. Usually, I would pose a question and call on someone to share a response, and then ask if anyone wanted to add to the discussion or had a question. The students would take it from there. They shared great ideas that led to deep questions. This was harder to come by naturally early in the school year because the students weren't used to this class format. Sometimes I would jump in and ask the class a question or change the direction of where they were going. As the year went on, the students realized that it was okay for them to lead the discussion and engage in a sophisticated dialogue about what they read. Often, they would carry the discussion into the hall after the bell rang and class was over.

Teaching different styles of writing to all of the grade levels reminded me why I love writing so much. Thinking about those specific lessons is hard for me as I sit and write about it now, bringing up so many memories of a time I wish I could relive. Writing this book is the new adventure of how I can actively create my path back into writing and teaching.

I am a teacher and I will always be a teacher at my core and in my soul. Nobody else can redefine me or take that away. The people who only see me as someone with a brain injury will never take away my passion or talent. Most importantly, nothing can erase the students who I've taught throughout the years, the impact I hope to have made on them, and the lives they impact.

Chapter 4
Support Team

Cultivating a support team is crucial. My husband, family, friends, and doctors make up the strongest team in which I keep placing my life. My support team catches me more often than they will ever realize and saves me from falling apart before I do. One of the most important lessons I have learned in ten years is that I don't need to do everything alone in order to succeed. I need the people who love me to remind me that I am not broken, especially when I forget. I rely on reassurance because I am different and exist in my new normal. I need to know this help will always be there to hold me up.

I refer to my support team specifically as a team, not just a support system. We work and communicate together, keeping everyone involved each step of the way along my journey. My doctors consult with each other regarding my treatment and progress. Family and friends talk to each other, making game-time decisions together as the playing field changes and that will hopefully benefit me at any given moment.

Bob is the anchor of my team. Standing six-feet-tall, he can hug me and hold me providing such security that he takes my pain away, and I forget about all of the challenges ahead for those few minutes. Bob was able to take time from work to stay with me throughout the summer. Since then, he has attended every hospital visit with me, calmed me down during each exam or test, and explained anything I may have misunderstood from the doctor's appointment. He is always there to support me, especially on my days when I feel weak, helping me walk down the hall safely to each appointment, and then back to our car.

Bob and I met in 2001 while working in college admission counseling. He is easy-going, happy, and brilliant. We worked at the same school in 2003 in Connecticut. We started dating and just a few months later he proposed at the beach while we were in San Diego on Easter vacation. We returned to school after the long weekend, and halfway through teaching my class, my students noticed my sparkly new engagement ring.

One of them screamed mid-lesson, "Ms. Loiaconi!" "Is that an engagement ring?"

"Yes, it is," I replied.

"What's his name?" They pushed since they had all spent months gossiping if Bob and I were dating.

"Mr. Hurley."

The girls screamed and shrieked with such excitement and happiness for us, and all ran up to me to see the ring. Within seconds, every student in the school packed into my classroom asking for every detail. The room was bursting with so much energy that the rest of the faculty came running into the room.

One student ran to Bob's office to congratulate him and drag him down the hall with the rest of the school. The students at our school were so excited for us that they ran our engagement announcement in the school newspaper.

We got married on November 13, 2004 in New York, and it was the first snow of the year that season. My brother spent the morning shoveling ice and snow off our mom's porch in his tuxedo and winter coat. Our wedding was exactly as we wanted; beautiful and focused on family and friends.

The vows to love each other in sickness and in health stay true to Bob's heart, and I am forever grateful. He is the most hopeful person who always sees the silver lining in every situation.

Bob and I never saw this accident coming and weren't prepared for all of the complications and fear that changed our world in an instant.

He selflessly puts me and my care above anything on his personal or professional schedules. Every day he looks at me, saying he is proud of me. So often, I ask him why he says that, because I don't think I've done anything special. Bob holds my hand and reassures me that I will be all right and he will always be here for me.

I mustered up the courage one day to ask him if he is disappointed that I haven't made more progress during the years and if he was happier with our life before the brain injury. He looked me in the eyes and just shook his head. He held my hand and smiled, telling me that he loves me, and loves the life we built together. As my team anchor, he empowers me to keep moving forward every day, especially when I have a hard day.

My mom is strength personified. She handles emergencies like a pro and gets everything under control so fast that I often forget I'm in a life-threatening crisis. I wish I didn't cause her the stress and pain of watching me suffer in 2008. Of course, I wish Bob or anyone else didn't have to deal with it either. But I especially wish my mom didn't. She has had her fill of family to watch over, nurse call stations to put on speed dial, and uncomfortable plastic chairs to spend hours in.

Every morning she diligently waited for the doctors to make their rounds. With her notepad and pen in hand, she was ready with her list of questions about my condition and progress. Her list grew longer each night as she updated the rest of our family who sought more details and just wanted someone to tell them that I would be all right.

When I got home and learned the specifics of my hospital stay, I felt awful because I knew my mom had powered through this pain when her parents were ill. Most of all, in 2001, she spent four months visiting the hospital when my father, Steve Loiaconi, unexpectedly suffered heart disease, went into a coma for months, and passed away.

Now, she sat at my bedside while I was in a coma with possible brain damage.

Family members and friends came to visit me while I initially recovered at home. Sadly, to me, I don't even remember. Bob told me that Stephen flew out right away from Virginia and slept on our couch. He got on a flight so quickly that he forgot to pack a toothbrush.

My younger brother, and only sibling, Stephen, twenty-seven years old at the time, was working as a media journalist and studying to complete his Master of Fine Arts in writing degree at George Mason University in Virginia. He has always been very smart and a hard worker under any circumstances, a value instilled by both of our parents.

Stephen and I got along growing up and never fought about anything, but it wasn't until we both got older that we developed more common interests that brought us closer.

Both of us focused our undergraduate education at different schools in English literature and writing, and then we worked in New York City at our first jobs after college in media writing. He ultimately moved to Manhattan and onto another company, and I moved into my own apartment eventually becoming a teacher. We supported each other, and our mom, through our father's illness and passing. That experience certainly brought us closer, creating a strong sibling bond that will never be broken.

Dad would be very proud of Stephen for many reasons.

With teaching us that family always comes first, and following suit like our mom, Stephen functions more in the archetypal role of a big brother to me than I his big sister to him.

Similarly, to Bob, he quickly learned the adaptations that my body required resulting from the TBI, most notably how quickly my stamina dropped. Stephen holds a keen steadiness about him, which I still rely on, and am grateful for, to this day. He can calm me down when I start to panic.

He takes over a situation when he sees that I get overwhelmed, provides me a strong arm with which to walk, and is resourceful to find or create a safe spot for me to rest when I am drained.

Since I didn't have the energy or strength to stand up or walk by myself after being released from the hospital, my doctor recommended that two people initially be with me in the house for safety. My mom was concerned that she might not be physically strong enough to brace my body if I collapsed while she was helping me walk. She stayed in San Diego with us for six weeks to help with my recovery until I was well enough to only need one person's support during the day. It was bittersweet when she left because I didn't know if I could make progress without her, but it also meant I was strong enough that she could leave me and return to living her life.

Dad is my guardian angel. Telling stories of dad keeps my father's memory alive, and what pushes me to get stronger is that I want to make my dad proud. I want to hold the same values of hard work close to my heart for my parents' sake.

Sharing this experience from the beginning with my mom, even the parts I don't remember, brings back so many memories of my father. When my mom and I reminisce about him now, she says my dad always told her I was resilient. He saw that I never gave into whatever stood in my way of completing a task, even at a young age. I put the extra time in, so I could find another way to reach my goal. I worked through what didn't go my way and was out of my control. I kept my head up with hope that the people supporting me wouldn't give up on me. That made a big difference.

When I didn't win, I got back up, brushed myself off, and moved forward down a different road. Being the 'best' or getting the 'highest grade' wasn't my focus. I wanted to earn the grade I worked for and always gave my best from start to finish. My father and I were very close, and he was really my first mentor. I looked up to him for advice and we even commuted on the same train together every morning for work when I lived in New York.

When I woke up from the coma, my mom told me that everyone we knew was praying for me across the country—including my brother, aunts, uncles, cousins, all of their friends, their kids, my dad's friends, their kids, and everyone's friends of friends.

I don't remember anything from being in the coma, but I felt, and still feel, the bond of so many people praying for me and caring about me together.

I believe my father heard those payers and pulled me out of the coma because my time wasn't up. I relied on him for strength as a little girl and I still rely on him today for strength. His belief in me is one of the reasons I have hope at the end of each day, even when it seems dark.

I look back at my baby pictures often so I never forget the value of family. My favorite part about these pictures is that my parents, aunts and uncles, grandparents and cousins all have huge beaming smiles. A tradition my parents started when Stephen and I were toddlers was to take a picture of us at each holiday in matching outfits at the same spot in the living room in our first house.

I also noticed a theme of my father's favorite hobby coming through in the pictures. There are more baby pictures than I can count of me holding golf clubs—baby sized and adult. To say he enjoyed playing golf is not nearly enough of a description.

Our house was filled with everything golf. Dad had a different club in each room and took practice swings whenever he had the chance. One morning he even took a practice swing through my fish bowl. He fell in love with playing golf as a thirteen-year-old caddy who had the course to himself on Mondays when the club was closed to members.

He told us that he spent those days diligently practicing the skills he learned during the week. Practice is how he became a strong golfer. My mom took up the game years later with him, and then Stephen and I started taking lessons.

Dad always told me I needed to learn to play golf so when I got my first job I wouldn't be the only woman in the office on Friday afternoons. I would instead be making decisions on the golf course, just like the male executives. He told me every day that I was intelligent, adaptable, and a hard worker.

Bob's parents are also valuable members of my support team. They always made sure I had company and would be safe. Bob's mother, Cecile, is a nurturing woman who dropped everything to tend to me.

She saw how uncertain I was, and how much I wanted my strength back. She was best at making me stay in bed. She kept reminding me that everyone was there to help, and she was always watching to make sure I didn't hurt myself.

I was, and still am, so thankful for how she looked after our household to make sure Bob and I were both doing okay. She knew how draining this situation was becoming on him, and she was selfless to help Bob take breaks.

We had a nice family system worked out, so I was constantly monitored, whether I was asleep or awake. Everyone took turns relieving each other. This allowed for Bob's parents to have a night to themselves or for my mom to have a night off. This also gave Bob and his dad, Don, time to go to a San Diego Padres baseball game every few nights.

Bob loves baseball. He was a New York Mets fan growing up and has been a Padres season ticket holder since before we were married. He collects baseball memorabilia, anything from signed baseballs and rookie cards to bats and jerseys. Our season tickets are on the second level at Petco Park along the third base line.

This is a big 'foul ball' area, so most people around us, including Bob, sit with their baseball gloves open and ready to catch a foul ball. Bob never goes to a game without his glove. He caught a ball once and gave it to a child sitting in front of him. I don't go to very many of the games with Bob as he takes his dad to most of the games. I'll join them from time to time with some mutual friends on nights when we have extra tickets.

Other than baseball, Bob's other hobby is playing tennis. We have four courts in the backyard at our condo complex, so it is convenient for his friends to come over after work. He usually hits for two hours at least three times a week. He watches various tennis tournaments on TV and insisted that our cable package include the Tennis Channel.

Because of my support team, I started feeling stronger. I also started getting cabin fever so I made a list of projects to do in the house that didn't involve a lot of energy or too much physical activity. One night, when Bob took his mom to dinner, his father, Don, spent the evening with me to tackle item No. 1 on my list. I ordered a clothes drying rack that I couldn't assemble by myself. The pieces were too heavy for me so Don put it together while I watched. I still have the drying rack and think of him every time I use it. That night was a milestone in my recovery because it was the first time I checked an item off my to-do list since the July 10 fall.

I am blessed with incredible friends who I respect, trust, learn from, thank, aspire to, and love. It's hard to find someone you can really trust, to the point that you can share your soul-to-the-core with no questions asked, who will be present for longer than one year. I'm fortunate that my true friends support me in every way, cheer me on even when I've only completed a simple task, build me up, help me advocate, and feel my setbacks when I have them.

I have trust in the universe that these special people—true friends—keep coming into my life at the exact moments they are meant to and have never turned their backs. I still have the cards sending prayers, good wishes and messages to get well soon. So many friends and friends of family sent beautiful flowers to cheer me up and brighten my house. My new healing sanctuary held an aromatic essence of strength, faith, and support. The flowers and cards brought the entire world directly into my home and heart instantly.

Support can't exist in a vacuum with one person running the show and without everyone working together. Most importantly, support doesn't work without including the patient.

These are the reasons why I value and appreciate my support team and friends so much. They are there for me all of the time with compassion and energy, devoted to rooting me on. During the past ten years, I've tried expressing gratitude to my support team for always being there and not abandoning me.

The most hopeful attribute of a support team is that the members are not static or finite. The people on my support team love me unconditionally, even when I feel like I don't deserve their selfless compassion. The only way I translate how much meaning is behind my words when I say to anyone on my team, "Thank you for supporting me," is to look them in the eye with a big smile and a few tears, hug them tightly and for a little too long, before giving an extra silent squeeze with a built-in understood, "I love you."

Chapter 5
Becoming a Healthcare Advocate

I redefined what it meant to look for a second opinion. As a TBI survivor, one of the most important things I need is for my doctors and nurses to please listen when I try to explain the type of pain I experience or help I need. For the first two years of doctors' appointments, I had so much trouble keeping track of conversations that I feared the doctor would explain something I wouldn't understand or remember, so Bob joined me at my doctor's appointments and always brought a notepad.

An additional challenge of the TBI was to find a neurologist for follow-up care after coming home from the hospital. I didn't have a clue where to start—how did I find a specialist in an area I've never needed? I finally found a doctor and went to 7:00 a.m. appointments every other week for two years. My husband came into the exam room with me to help explain some things I had trouble understanding from my doctor.

After two years, my seizures had not improved under this doctor's care. I endured countless doses of medications that didn't help me and caused horrific side effects. When my hair started falling out and I could not keep food down, I called to say I needed to stop taking one of the pills, so he increased the dose of the other. Later I learned that those medications don't treat TBI-related epileptic seizures.

During one appointment—which became our last appointment—that doctor accused me of faking my seizures to get my husband's attention and said there was nothing neurologically wrong with me.

He referred to me as the boy who cried wolf, claiming that people would eventually stop listening to my pleas for help while I was seizing. The only words I could sputter out of my mouth were, "That kid got eaten!" Then he said to make an appointment for two weeks from that day. I asked why I would do that when he just informed me I had nothing neurologically wrong? His only response was to walk away. Before we walked out, I signed the form requesting a copy of medical records be mailed to me.

When I started reading the two-inch thick file, I was shocked that there was no mention of my TBI. I felt violated by him, so I continued my search for someone to care for me. This became much more of an arduous journey than expected.

I saw four neurologists, took a fifteen-hour exam, and underwent a five-day; sleep deprived video EEG only to be told that I didn't have epileptic seizures. Test after test came up with the same result and I started to hate the word 'inconclusive.' My blood boiled each time one of so many specialists gave me the news that the recent battery of tests was inconclusive to give a specific diagnosis for the latest game the TBI was playing on my body. Every few years, a ping-pong match starts and new symptoms arise for new inexplicable conditions that send me to another set of tests.

I knew that something wasn't right. None of these doctors focused on the TBI. Finally, the sixth doctor I found was a TBI specialist on our insurance plan who happened to be the neurologist who treated me in the ER back in 2008. He immediately pulled up my brain scan from that night and prescribed, at the time, a leading anti-seizure drug that none of the other doctors had. I've improved greatly under his care since 2011. I knew my body and needed to fight for myself.

I decided to make each experience a learning point. Now, I take detailed notes at every doctor appointment I have, including writing the date and stapling my receipt to the notes. I also am confident to ask someone to please repeat or explain something so that I am certain I understand correctly. I never leave an appointment without asking what the next step is for my care.

After years of struggling with the ataxia, my neurologist sent me for six weeks of physical therapy in 2014 hoping it would help strengthen my imbalance caused by the ataxia. I arrived at the physical therapy and rehabilitation center for my first hour-long session eager to meet the therapist and hopeful her expertise could improve this one area of my life. That being my first time in physical therapy, I didn't know what to expect, so I was perplexed to spend the first half of my session explaining the specifics of my condition.

I didn't question the professional. I was just happy to stand up and spend time moving after all of the talking, considering that it was physical therapy. The therapist was present and took notes about the balance challenges I'd experienced. Next was the assessment of my current balance level, which surprised her. It also surprised me that TBI-related deficits were not widely understood.

We moved on and she taught me four stretches for my core and legs to practice while lying down at home daily until my next session the following week. As our time was up, and before I had the chance to ask any questions about the stretches, I made a point to confirm that she would be my therapist throughout the program. I explained my concern of starting over each week explaining everything to someone new.

She assured me that if for some reason she was out, everything we discussed would be documented in my file, so a different therapist would be completely up to speed.

And each Wednesday at 1:00 p.m. after I checked in at the front office of the physical therapy and rehabilitation center, I was greeted by a different therapist to whom I needed to explain my situation and start with a new series of exercises again and again.

After expressing my concern about this the second time and seeking clarification, the therapist explained that it must have been a one-time mistake that day. I also asked why she didn't continue with the four stretches I'd been practicing. She wanted to evaluate my core strength with standing exercises.

That made sense to me, and so when she asked me to stand on a platform and grab the handlebars, I did so. She quickly said that the platform would rock back and forth with other distractions, but I should hold the bars and work to stabilize my core. The second my hands reached the handlebars, the platform shook like an earthquake, with flashing lights and noises. I yelled out to stop, reminding her I have a seizure condition that all of the stimuli trigger. She looked perplexed that I didn't want to continue that day and sent me home, trembling.

The following three weeks followed similar suit and I couldn't wait for the program to end. I was determined to complete the full six weeks because I didn't want to give up on any treatment available to me, plus I was so overwhelmed that I felt lost and helpless. The therapist I met at my sixth session was different in that he asked many detailed questions about my TBI and about what exercises I'd done so far. He was shocked and confused at my program to date, explaining that the moving platform, plus other exercises, is not safe for someone with a TBI and seizure condition. He went on to explain that he was a TBI-specific physical therapist. I never knew such a specialty existed and how much he could help me progress. My insurance did not approve another round of physical therapy, but I knew from then on to always request a TBI specialist for any physician, therapist, or radiologist.

I also learned I have the right to ask what medication I am given.

I remember sitting in an ER one night refusing to take pills handed to me by a nurse who didn't read my file correctly and mixed up my medication schedule. Her mistake would have changed the levels of my anti-seizure medications in my blood for the next twelve hours. From then on, the first, and usually only, request I make is that the doctors and nurses please listen when I am asking for help because sometimes I have trouble communicating clearly. The reality is that if I am the only person who can speak for and understand me, then I am truly the best person to advocate for my care. This is my healthcare, doctors, treatment, medication, hospital care, therapy, and diagnosis. If something doesn't feel right to me, as the patient, I have the right to speak up and ask for clarification.

Open and clear communication with each of my doctors and the wonderful people who work in their offices has helped raise my confidence in and education of my healthcare. Since I need to keep records of any lab or hospital tests or scans, I've learned that the most effective and organized way to do so is to ask at the registration desk upon check in to please have a copy of the day's results mailed home. Sometimes there is a patient release or waiver to sign, but this is so much easier than backtracking and making phone calls to hunt for every test result throughout the years.

I always ask my doctors to please explain to me what test or procedure they are ordering or performing, and why, so that I can understand more about my condition and treatments. It's smart to become as informed as possible regarding the specifics of my current state of health but learning from legitimate and up-to-date websites is important as well. Again, I ask my doctors and other healthcare professionals what resources they recommend for me to find credible education. When I arrive at one of the suggested websites, usually a nonprofit or educational research institution, I read the 'about us' and 'contact us' links to give myself context within which I am learning.

The nonprofit brain injury foundations are great sources of education as well. I've found it helpful to join the local and national foundations so I can stay abreast of news and updates where I live, but also learn about trends on a bigger scale. The San Diego Brain Injury Foundation (SDBIF) has an abundance of resources for anyone affected by a brain injury. They maintain information for many types of specialists, rehabilitative services, and monthly support group meetings.

I've learned that connecting with a local foundation can help propel one's confidence for how to speak to health professionals and open doors to private health events and speaking engagements that are for members only.

I want to play as active a role as possible in my recovery, especially when there are so many days I don't have the strength, and so many things out of my control. I continue learning about the many facets of brain injury recovery, which then enables me to become a resource for other survivors.

Chapter 6
Physical Comeback

Every day of this journey brings me opportunities to awaken new sides of myself that I might never have had the courage to look at before. I was bedridden for more than a month while recovering in 2008. When I was ready to start building my strength back up, I walked to the YMCA next door to our condominium complex and took a few group exercise classes. My stamina was very low and I could barely walk in a straight line since my coordination was poor. I felt defeated after taking a few classes. I never liked group exercise when I was healthy. I was never a coordinated person. I was self-conscious, believing people were watching me to see if I was doing the steps wrong.

Plus, I couldn't stand the boring low-energy music. The added challenge of needing to nail the steps with an injured brain made me check out of every class. After trying one of each group exercise class offered from A to Z, the only one left was Zumba®, the cardio dance fitness class of Latin and World rhythms. I was nervous, not only because I was weak physically, but I had no background experience as a dancer. The class description read this was a total workout, combining all elements of fitness—cardio, muscle conditioning, balance, and flexibility in an interval-style calorie-burning workout. That meant nothing to me and went right over my head.

I didn't know anything about Zumba®, but wanted to give it a fair chance. Slowly, and a little wobbly, I walked into the wide-open mirrored room with red stars on the floor, each marking a spot for a participant. I stood on a star in the back. The students surrounding me smiled and introduced themselves, and then the instructor, Ninfa Skezas, greeted the class.

Her vibrant voice was welcoming, cheerful, and encouraging from the start. She turned the music on and told us to all take a deep breath and make a big smile. The music ran through my body and energized the whole room for the next hour. My body was only able to handle the basic step tapping side-to-side, and I left feeling like a rock star.

Ninfa and the other students smiled and cheered me on. It lifted up my spirits and before I realized, the hour was over. Even though I didn't follow the steps perfectly, I still felt empowered to introduce myself to the instructor after class while a few other students stayed to socialize. That night, socialize took on new meaning for me, and from then on, became a word I would never take lightly because it had been missing from my life in such a personal context.

That first Zumba® class in 2008 changed me. That was the first time I felt alive and not sick since my tragic fall. Little did I know at the time how close I would hold that first class to my heart and how relevant that moment would still be for me. I also didn't realize that night would bring someone very special into my life, and onto my support team.

I kept taking classes with Ninfa and over time, I shared my story with her; a story only eight weeks in the making. We bonded right away and she quickly became one of my closest friends. I still take her Zumba® classes today.

Ninfa is more than a Zumba® instructor to me. We met when I was at my weakest; when I was just beginning my physical and rehabilitative process in September 2008. Ninfa is a special woman whose heart is filled with optimism and radiates pure selflessness in every moment. It is an honor to be her friend, and I count myself lucky for her unwavering loyalty and compassion throughout the years. I have been able to reach my strongest peaks with her support.

Ninfa and I have been through every adventure imaginable, and some beyond, and by the end of every day, we check in to make sure each other is okay, especially when one of us is struggling. She is a true friend and we call each other sister, rather our mothers do.

Her mother visits from Venezuela for a few months at a time each year, and my mom visits from New York a few times a year. We introduced the two of them in 2010. Shortly thereafter my mom was taking lessons in introductory Spanish from Ninfa and her mother.

It was a joy to watch our moms together because they hugged and smiled so much at each other, without needing to talk. When they are in town, the four of us often have lunch together. Other friends join from time to time and Ninfa's mother introduces me as her other daughter. To me, the most beautiful part about my friendship with Ninfa is that our mothers supported each other as they learned the other's native languages. My family and support team were growing.

Another family who accepted me right away as one their own was my new Zumba® family. The Zumba® family is hard to explain to people because it is so simple. We welcome new people to classes with warm smiles and open arms to join the fun. I never had that before.

All my life I was the weak kid, not an athlete, picked last—not wanted as part of a team. It made me feel inadequate and afraid to try anything new for fear of failure. That is not who I am anymore. My accident changed how I approach life and gave me the wisdom and courage not to hold myself back.

I took a leap of faith to see if I could pass the training to become a licensed Zumba® instructor. I was so nervous I wouldn't pass, that I didn't tell anyone I was even trying out for it. I stayed in bed for two full days before the training to conserve my energy, packed lots of snacks and water, and arrived at the gym half an hour early.

I was so nervous throughout the non-stop, eight-hour training day. It took a real toll on my body. By the end of the day, I was convinced I didn't pass. I felt total pain and exhaustion, and just wanted Bob to pick me up and carry me to bed. Then the trainer, holding my certificate, called my name as one of the newest licensed Zumba® instructors. I was sweating so much in the picture I took with her, but I didn't care.

I passed. I walked outside, got in the car, dropped my head into Bob's hands and burst into tears. So many emotions mixed with pain, soreness, and exhaustion ran through my body that I didn't know what to say. Bob just kept telling me how proud he was of me and held my hand.

In October 2009, I reached my first goal on my journey to recovery, and I didn't stop there. I joined my instructor's Zumba® dance group to perform at local events in the community. I was elated to be part of a team working together and be strong enough just to dance in one or two songs with the group. It was a huge step forward.

In 2010, I started teaching my own Zumba® class free of charge in the community building at my condo complex. The class was open to our neighbors and the public, plus people who couldn't afford a gym membership could join this class. It was important for me to give back for what Zumba® did, and still does, for me.

My students created a welcoming community that I'm so proud to foster. I still have a passion to this day to host charity events annually in San Diego to help others and bring people together.

Dance fitness became a big part of surviving and thriving in my new normal, plus it was the first benchmark of my physical comeback from the trauma I'd endured. During the next few years, I suffered further falls that made it a little harder to stand up and dance. I made a promise to myself that I will always make the choice to stand up and be fearless.

In 2015, I took my first U-Jam Fitness® class, stumbling through every second and loving it. I emailed the instructor that night thanking her for the class and said I wouldn't come back because I wasn't ready or coordinated enough for it.

She was so encouraging from the start and replied that I did great, brought so much energy, and really should come to class again. Like Zumba®, I knew U-Jam Fitness® would help me with my self-care. But the workouts seemed out of reach and the financial obligation was too much for me.

Without these two fitness programs, I wouldn't be strong enough or in the correct mindset to enjoy my life without the noise. My physical therapy program was about to end, and I knew I needed to rely on these programs. That was exactly when Project Athena Foundation (PAF) came into my life.

A nonprofit dedicated to helping women survivors of medial or other traumatic setbacks achieve their adventurous dreams, PAF pushed me even further to achieve a fitness goal I never thought possible. PAF generously funded my grant proposal for U-Jam Fitness® instructor training, as the financial obligation was holding me back. U-Jam Fitness® is a cardio dance workout set to world rhythms with an urban backdrop and culture.

When people ask me what U-Jam Fitness® is, I explain that it is a cardio dance fitness class, and so much more. The mission is, "Changing Lives One Beat at a Time." I wanted to be a U-Jam Fitness® instructor since taking my first class in 2015. Everyone who walks into a class is surrounded by welcoming energy and a unity before the workout begins. Their focus is in line with that of PAF, which is why I'm so passionate about both programs.

The support of the PAF family and the U-Jam Fitness® family boosted my confidence to push through the rigorous athletic physical and mental adventure. The instructor certification includes a nine-hour training day, learning cueing and choreography, coaching and post-training follow up. There was so much to learn and absorb about the precision, safety skills, stamina, and fitness intensity.

Executing these four types of instruction at the same time would require much-needed concentration. That was just the basic level. Then we spent a lot of time learning about the importance of a good instructor versus an inspirational instructor. That was the key moment I really felt the missions of PAF and U-Jam Fitness® in my heart. There was constant support through this process from current instructors reaching out as mentors to help me prepare for the big day.

I actually hit an obstacle four days before my training when the pain on my left side due to a previous injury returned.

I was at a practice session with my coach, who was a true rock for me, when I told him about stabbing pain I felt and that I was wearing my pain patches for the first time since the eight months when I finished physical therapy. I started crying and said I didn't know how to move forward with the training since I wouldn't be able to move in proper form. He said that we just needed to inform the trainer so she would be aware of my injury. Some people might have held off on the training for another month, but not this survivor.

Halfway through the training, my body felt such a high pain level that I really wanted to give up and go home because I was so overwhelmed. It hurt just to walk around the room that the thought of any more exercise with this program felt unrealistic. My coach, and dear friend, saw that I was having trouble. He told me to take a break, sat with me, got my ice pack, listened to my concerns and reminded me that I had the strength to persevere.

I took a deep breath, hit 'reset' and was present with the rest of the group without a second thought. I passed my training and took my comeback to the next level. I will always be sincerely grateful to PAF for the opportunity to reach that dream of being an instructor.

I'm one of the lives that U-Jam Fitness® changed and now I want to change another life, one beat at a time. I am working hard as a TBI advocate and want to use my voice to share my experiences with a larger population to inspire, evolve or ignite a call to action of positivity in our current culture. Through U-Jam Fitness® I am pushing farther than I thought possible. Merging the cognitive and physical aspects of the choreography feels like a miracle every time I look in the mirror.

At times I still feel frustrated and get discouraged when certain steps don't sync correctly, but I have faith that it will come together. I became an instructor to reach the next step in my recovery so I can give back and make a difference by providing even one person with inspiration to try for that out-of-reach brass ring and not give up. The mission of the Project Athena Foundation became a part of me and my physical comeback. I am a survivor and Project Athena helped realize I am a fighter. I am fierce. I am not broken. I am stronger.

The word support has a tangible meaning to me that I didn't understand before. Everyone in PAF championed me to succeed in my training more than I thought I could.

I honestly walked into the room on adventure day feeling the support of PAF with me. I am more confident, not only in the fitness arena of my adventure, but as a woman who grew up feeling inadequate. The people from PAF taught me to enhance my calling to help others, give from my experiences, and try to make a difference for someone. I carry the name Athena, bestowed upon me by PAF, with great pride.

One of the biggest gifts PAF gave me is to examine the word 'comeback' in context for the first time. My U-Jam Fitness® instructor adventure challenged and supported me to keep fighting the physical capacities I lost with the TBI. I've worked hard to earn those back and surpass where I started. I'm sharing this new strength in our community as a volunteer, team member and educator. I don't feel alone anymore while having a tough day.

Becoming a dance fitness instructor in both of these formats blessed me by allowing me to return to the world of teaching. When I put on my Zumba® and U-Jam Fitness® clothes, I transform into a superhero. The uniform of neon colors, crazy patterns, and bright red shirts unleash my super powers of resilience, confidence, and invincibility.

My job is to stand strong, lead my students with pride, build their confidence, and find their superpowers. I stand tall in my bright colors.

When I was a high school teacher, I never liked wearing a pair of sneakers because I didn't feel comfortable in them. My students loved my clothes. They weren't expensive or flashy, but trendy enough with nice shoes. I felt like a superhero in that uniform everyday guiding students to become free thinkers as they read classics in American literature.

But I needed to trade in my heels from my high school teaching days for multi-colored sneakers to look for work.

Dance fitness became part of my rehabilitative therapy, as it was during those classes that I began to make my comeback, gaining stamina and strength so I could become a licensed instructor. I grew into leading fundraising events in the community and teaching classes free of charge. It's important to me to give back for everything the dance fitness community did, and still does, for me. I believe I can reach a wider audience locally, and hopefully globally, through dance fitness.

My goal is to champion for unity, peace, respect, encouragement and teamwork for others. I never thought I would find myself in the dance fitness world, as I never enjoyed it or did well athletically. If I hadn't been accepted and welcomed for who I was inside as a person in 2008, I wouldn't have gone back and don't know where I'd be now. My Zumba® and U-Jam Fitness® families feed my soul.

When friends look at pictures of me taken during these events, they tell me that I look like I'm glowing and have never looked happier, especially when I'm not looking at the camera. Those are the greatest compliments I've heard in years because those pictures show me feeling happy and being confident in the moment.

I'm proud to be a leader in my community expressing my personal Zumba® and U-Jam Fitness® styles while championing a healthy lifestyle and showing people it's okay to break out sometimes. Our clothes are just the starting point that develops the Zumba® and U-Jam Fitness® cultures. The music, energy and inclusion make each their own communities, welcoming others without judgment. I really felt like Megan again for the first time in a long time. The spring of 2017 had a great amount of promise. Physically, I was at the strongest point I'd been in a few years.

Then, at the start of July 2017, my body slowly began to decline. My neurologist tried to work out the correct dose of my seizure medications since my focal seizures were becoming more frequent. For the rest of the summer, I showed up for my 7:30 a.m. blood draw appointment every ten to fourteen days. The people at the lab referred to me as a 'frequent flyer' since I was there so often. This was very hard on my mind and body.

With every change he made in dosage, my white cell count became dangerously low. Finally, with the right dosage, my white cell count slowly worked up to being slightly acceptable.

In September 2017, I started feeling good again and back on track. My mom came to visit me in San Diego for a week and we had a relaxing and fun visit. We went to her favorite restaurants and enjoyed the beautiful weather sitting outside in the fresh air.

My mom brought me to the lab for what would be my last blood test on September 18, 2017, and the next day she flew home to New York. The neurologist called with news that all of my blood levels were finally safe and everything was moving in the right direction.

Until that day, the only regret I had was that my mom wasn't with me for that phone call. That was, until three days later, Saturday, September 23, 2017, when Bob had to leave another message for mom.

Chapter 7
September 2017 Fall

While lightning might not strike twice, a head trauma certainly can. Nine years later, I sat once again on my shower chair and washed the dried blood out of my hair. It mixed with my tears of fear, awe, and total insecurity of what lies ahead as my broken teeth almost fell out of my mouth and water ran through the broken cavities of my face.

I met my friend, Kelly Tobey, at the San Diego Gaslamp Westin for a cup of coffee on Saturday September 23, 2018 at 8:30 a.m. before going to a seminar about nonprofit associations. The three-hour seminar was interesting, especially since it was an area of interest to both of us. We each took notes sitting in the big hotel conference room watching PowerPoint presentations. At the break, I sent a text to a friend from U-Jam Fitness® that I was feeling a little tired and dizzy, so I wouldn't attend our instructor event later that afternoon. I returned to my seat drinking a glass of water and snacking on a granola bar. I felt a slight surge of energy that kept me going through the rest of the workshop.

When the seminar let out at noon, Kelly and I decided to eat lunch at the hotel restaurant to compare our notes from the morning. We also thought that I would feel stronger and more like myself after eating a full meal. After two hours, I felt much better and more stable. We paid our bill and enjoyed a relaxing afternoon.

She pointed to a man walking his dog through the lobby and commented on the cuteness of the dog. I felt the double vision come on and I told her that, "I see three-and-a-half dogs. Something isn't right."

Right away, we got up, left the restaurant and walked directly outside to get a taxi home. We stood next to each other in front of the hotel, and without making a movement or taking the smallest step, the last thing I remember is yelling, "Kelly, help!" I collapsed down onto the pavement face-first from a straight standing position; breaking my nose, three front teeth and fracturing my remaining facial bones.

The hotel staff called 911 and Kelly called Bob immediately. He later told me that all he could hear was my screaming in the background of Kelly telling him that I fell and he needed to come to the hospital right away.

The paramedics separated Kelly and me; one stabilized me for safe transfer in the ambulance while the other tried to obtain my personal information from Kelly as she gathered my purse and the items that fell to the ground. Half of my navy-blue tote purse was soaked with my blood, and I left a red clotting pool of blood behind on the hotel pavement.

At first, Kelly climbed into the back of the ambulance to ride alongside me on the gurney. The paramedic told her that the only way she could ride in the ambulance was to sit in the front passenger seat with her seat belt buckled.

The next day, she told me how panicked and scared I was, and that I kept screaming out her name. She said that I was less agitated when she sat in the back of the ambulance with me for those few minutes holding my hand.

I started screaming more and became more afraid when the paramedics separated us. I remember screaming her name throughout the entire ride to the hospital in between moments of spitting out blood. I remember hearing her call back at me; trying to calm me down and assure me that everything was all right. She felt helpless and wanted nothing more than to hold my hand and nurture me through this trauma. Because of incidents like this, I wish everyone's name on my support team could fit on my medical bracelet. That action alone could add some humanity to an impersonal piece of jewelry, reminding the people who read it that I am a person with people in my life who love me, and not just a patient who will cycle in and out of an ambulance.

Bob made great time to the hospital. He actually pulled off the exit just as the ambulance passed by and saw Kelly sitting in the front seat.

Bob made that dreaded phone call to my mom for the second time in less than ten years, his hands and voice shaking, but he couldn't reach her. He left her a message that she needed to call him back right away because something terrible happened. They didn't connect on the phone until 8:00 p.m. when I was in the trauma ward. Bob explained the details of the accident and assured her that it was not necessary for her to fly back.

Even though he was still waiting for the radiology results, I was conscious, which was a much better condition than I had been in right after the fall in 2008. Bob hadn't called my brother at that point. He thought it was best that my mom heard the news of my accident first, rather than Stephen. She was actually on her way to visit Stephen and his wife, Airlie, in Virginia that day, which is why Bob couldn't reach her at first. We were both glad to find out that they were all together for the weekend while receiving updates of my condition.

I was admitted to the ER around 3:00 p.m. while Bob anxiously paced in the hallway, again, similarly to how he did in 2008. The doctors in the ER prioritized stopping the bleeding in the broken cavities of my face to stabilize me. Only then could they run the panel of tests including MRIs, CT scans, and X-Rays, among others. Similarly, to 2008, they kept me in a collar until my radiology scans were cleared to prevent paralysis.

When the doctors came to update Bob on my status, he handed them my seizure medication that he brought from home—he never wanted me to miss a dose. They finally brought Bob in from the waiting room around 5:00 p.m. to sit with me before moving me to the upstairs trauma ward.

He left a message for our dentist detailing what happened and that the surgeons said I would need to see him as soon as possible to fix the broken teeth. He also left messages for my neurologist, psychiatrist, and primary care physician about this accident.

I was unconscious from the time the ambulance brought me into the hospital. After being treated in the ER and while undergoing the various tests, I woke up in my bed in the trauma ward around 7:00 p.m. on Saturday, September 23, 2017 with Bob holding my hand. I didn't know where I was at first, and within a few minutes, the whole day came screaming back and I remembered exactly what happened.

Then, an intense feeling of terror took over because I didn't know the extent of my injuries. I was in wrenching pain. My face was so swollen that I could barely open my eyes.

My lips were swollen and severely cut that I could taste blood in my mouth. I couldn't move my upper body which was trapped in a collar. I started to panic, so Bob and the doctors patiently walked me through what happened and that I hadn't sustained more serious injuries.

He stayed with me until 12:30 a.m. before the hospital staff sent him home. All I wanted to do was sleep, but I kept slipping down in the bed from the collar.

I couldn't prop myself up comfortably, and the controls to adjust the bed were out of my reach. I needed to remain still, wearing the collar until they received detailed radiology results of my brain, neck and spine. I couldn't drink any water through a straw or have any ice chips until those scans came back in case they needed to operate on me.

I remember being so thirsty and my mouth felt like water had never passed through my lips before. I started to value the scans being clear just so I could drink water instead of the bigger picture that I wouldn't be paralyzed.

I wanted so much to just go to sleep, but my body was too uncomfortable. Every muscle ached and the noise in the ward reverberated like the inside of an echo chamber.

At some point, I either fell asleep or passed out from pain and dehydration.

I remember waking up at 6:00 a.m. the next morning when the doctor came to my bed with the radiology results. Since visiting hours hadn't started, I was alone to hear the news. My glasses couldn't rest on my broken face, so I couldn't even see the doctor when she told me the scans were clear and that I would not be paralyzed.

Bob returned to my hospital bed at 7:30 a.m. on Sunday with a smoothie, hoping that I would be cleared to drink something at that point, since I couldn't eat any food because of my broken teeth. Bob texted my mom some pictures of me in the hospital bed while I was sleeping so that she could see the extent of my injuries. She was afraid I would look much worse based on the description of the accident, so the pictures gave her a slight sense of comfort. We were overwhelmed in the hospital because two different plastic surgeons met with us regarding my broken nose, which the trauma ward didn't treat since it wasn't considered a priority.

The first surgeon said that I needed to contact my insurance company for a referral to any plastic surgeon right away. The next day, another plastic surgeon said we needed to wait at least two weeks for the swelling to go down and get a referral from my primary care physician. We just wanted to get home at that point and away from the confusion. I spent two days in the hospital, coming home on Sunday night, but it felt like months before I went home. Bob took Monday off from work to stay with me since I couldn't move around well or see through my swollen eyes, and he was worried about me being alone.

The fall in 2017 was different from my first fall. I don't remember anything from the 2008 experience. The 2017 incident is more personal because I recall the horrific details. I remember spitting blood out of my mouth in the ambulance and hearing Kelly's voice as she tried to calm me.

I can still envision the paramedic restraining my arms and telling me to stop moving around. I recall waking up not long after being in the hospital and feeling the collar at my neck and hearing Bob's voice while he held my hand. I remember every detail of the small trauma ward with only curtains surrounding each bed for privacy.

The nurses were great but did not stop talking and had to fight with many patients. There was a sick woman from Vietnam with two little boys next to me.

Across from me was an older man who screamed in pain every half hour when the nurses needed to turn him over. And to my left was the drunk, frightening man who yelled and cursed at everyone until he finally ripped out his IV and walked around the floor in just his tattooed body, backing hospital security off while he left without signing the American Medical Association form in which a patient chooses to leave the hospital before the treating physician recommends discharge.[12]

I remember getting up and seeing myself in the mirror for the first time and going home in just two days. There are no empty days, no large blocks of the experience that I do not remember. That is why I keep reliving it all over again throughout the recovery.

Chapter 8
2017 Transition Home

We had been living in San Diego for more than ten years when I came home from the hospital after this fall. I still felt just as far away from my family and friends back in New York than I did in 2008, when Bob and I started notifying everyone of what happened and we waited until I was home to contact most people. It was easier that way since Bob wasn't allowed to talk on his cell phone in the hospital, and we could both email people when we were home.

When I came home from the hospital in September 2017 things weren't much different. Bob and I didn't know what would help or hinder my healing. In March 2018, I learned of resources available to some brain injury survivors that I never learned about during the years from which I could have benefited greatly.

Nutritional therapy is something I should have pushed for in 2008 and in the following years, especially in 2017 when my teeth broke, and I couldn't chew. Part of this ten-year journey includes struggling with finding the best nourishment to get enough protein into my body for my endocrine, circulatory, and nervous systems to recover and rebuild.

I tried to sleep as much as possible, but unfortunately, I couldn't stay in bed. I was in such severe pain that long periods of sleep didn't come easy for me. Consciousness didn't allow for escapism to step away from reality and hope that the whole nightmare was a dream. In 2008, at least I slept in my own bed. Bob made many accommodations; most helpful was buying new pillows to support my weakened body.

This time, I had to sleep in the recliner chair in the den by myself. It was the only piece of furniture in the house where I could prop my head up to help reduce the swelling. It was also the only place I could prop my body up enough to find some capacity of comfort. I resented the chair and only planned to sleep there for a couple of nights.

Two days after being discharged from the trauma ward, I went to the dentist with hopes that he would somehow be able to stabilize my teeth before they fell out. Bob came with me to help explain what happened since I could barely open my swollen mouth to talk. I tried to open my lips as much as possible, the bloody cuts only halfway healed so the dentist tried taking the best set of X-rays possible.

It hurt so much just to bite down on the X-ray film, but I knew how important it was for the dentist to have at least a partial image of my teeth. I felt like I reached a goal by opening and closing my mouth enough for the film. The pain was worth it; the dentist saw the broken teeth, which thankfully didn't have nerve damage. My teeth and gums were too traumatized to withstand any dental procedures, but he wanted to find a solution to keep my teeth in place temporarily before I left his office.

He built a bracket that he glued behind my three front broken teeth to stabilize them while they hopefully would build back from the inside, similarly to how a cast functions. That meant no chewing for at least three months. My nutrition regimen consisted of smoothies, soup, yogurt, and ice cream until the week before Christmas, when I was able to start chewing a little bit.

Bob's parents, Cecile and Don, were a wonderful support team for us during this time. Since it was Bob's busy season at work, he went back to the office two days after bringing me home from the trauma ward.

His parents generously took care of our dog, Emmie, our seventeen-pound, thirteen-year-old Cavalier King Charles Spaniel, for more than a month until I could physically pick her up. I appreciated this help so much and Emmie had lots of fun at 'Grandma and Grandpa Camp.'

Bob's mom brought me fresh soup and smoothies each day, plus pudding or ice cream for dessert. She and Don also brought Emmie over for visits so I could pet her. That was all I could manage since it hurt too much for her little pink tongue to kiss my black and blue face.

My brother and his wife Airlie were very worried about me after mom told them what happened. Stephen and Airlie were married in 2015 and she has been one-hundred percent present for me. Stephen called Bob every day asking if I was going to be all right and if he should fly out to see me. I started taking selfies every day to send my family so they could see my progress as my wounds healed. Once I could talk again, I sent videos telling them I was getting a little better each day, but my teeth and mouth weren't healed enough to talk on the phone. My family took great comfort in this digital form of personal communication.

Everything felt like it cycled back to the blank unknown. This time I needed to find a plastic surgeon, which I never needed before and had no idea where to begin. We couldn't start with the leads from the hospital surgeons, because we received different sets of information, and their doctors wouldn't be covered under my insurance plan. When I started requesting referrals for the type of plastic surgeon specific to facial reconstruction, I kept receiving approvals for general plastic surgeons, none of whom specialized in facial bones.

More days and more weeks passed by, and my anxiety level grew higher without knowing if my broken bones would ever be fixed. I had no control over this daily uncertainty and how to manage it. I sat in a chair for what felt like a hopeless eternity. In real time, this eternity only amounted to ten extra business days until my appointment with the correct specialist for facial bones, mouth, and jaw injuries—a maxillofacial surgeon.

By the time I visited with the maxillofacial surgeon, the black and blue bruises on my face were gone, but there was still a lot of swelling. I was nervous preparing for this appointment because I was about to ask a man I had never met to bring at least some part of my appearance back to me.

I had no idea what lay ahead in terms of surgeries and pain, but I was turning my next 'new normal' over to him.

Before I fell in 2017, I looked exactly like my mom. I had her eyes and smile, but I had my father's cheekbone and jawbone structure. That was part of who I was and I did not want to lose that. My dad was already gone, and I needed to keep my mom in me forever.

The surgeon was very reassuring and calming. He could see how much pain I was in and how scared I was from the accident and the unknown ahead. My hands and voice shook as I showed him recent pictures of me and some of my mom with me. I wanted him to see the face I dreamed of getting back. I explained that I wasn't focused on vanity, but I wanted to maintain a little part of my previous identity, the one that mattered most.

Bob and I were so comforted by how much time the surgeon spent with us, how thoroughly he answered all of our questions and that he gave me a specific plan for at-home care. The best news that actually sounded too good to be true, was that he did not see a need or benefit to operate on me. He explained that since the surgeons in the trauma ward didn't operate on my broken nose within the first hour of the accident, he would need to break my nose and surrounding facial bones to repair it. He said this surgery would certainly cause me quite a lot of pain and wouldn't guarantee that the final outcome would look better than if we let my bones heal and settle on their own. This would also be the case with the other fractured facial bones. Bob and I gazed at him like deer in headlights with looks of disbelief that he wasn't going to operate.

The surgeon said that my face was still very swollen, and within another six weeks, if I followed the home care plan, we would see a big improvement. Before we left his office, we asked when we should make a follow up appointment. The surgeon told us there was no reason to do one—unless I had an emergency—because he would not operate on me. The emotions in the car on the drive home were so much lighter than the drive to the surgeon. Bob and I were so thankful that I would not need surgery, but very curious to see what the next six weeks would bring after following the surgeon's directions at home.

Step one was for me to stop wearing my glasses and start wearing my contacts again, as the glasses were counterproductive to my bones settling properly—the glasses were considered obstructions to my malleable bones. Consistent with the hospital surgeons, he also emphasized how important it was not to sneeze or blow my nose for another four weeks. He also agreed with my dentist that I drink Arnica tea and take Arnica supplements to reduce the swelling. I added another pill to my weekly case.

Everyone was right about this point, because those were magic pills and helped bring that swelling down faster than anticipated. Finally, I could see there was actually a chance that I might recover without surgery. This was new hope.

Unfortunately, the most important part of my home care plan propped me up and brought me down, feeling isolated, at the same time. He insisted that I keep sleeping in the recliner, even though I explained how uncomfortable it was. I needed to keep my head elevated at a forty-five-degree angle for the swelling, but mostly to remove the risk of my turning over and falling asleep on my face at all. Bob and Emmie slept in our bed in the next room. He and I were both devastated by not being together, especially when I was in so much pain. He kept offering to sleep on the inflatable mattress in the den so I wouldn't be alone. I thanked him so much for such a loving and sincere gesture, but he needed to be at work each morning and I didn't want him to be uncomfortable throughout the night.

Not to my surprise, the last part of how I was going to recuperate was to limit my exercise for a few months until my bones settled in place and my teeth re-set so there would be no danger of anything moving out of place. I found myself in a dark place after this fall for quite a few months.

I needed to stop teaching my volunteer Zumba® class, which is my rehabilitative therapy on top of my passion. I felt as though I'd let my students down more than ever and they might not come back when I tried to start teaching the class again. The pain was unbearable, I was alone most of the time, my face was gone, I constantly lived in a state of post-traumatic stress disorder (PTSD) from the trauma of the fall, and I couldn't take in any nourishment.

Looking back, the amazing part of my recovery is that I never gave up. I never packed it in, closed my computer and thought, "Oh well, I'm done trying, there is no point." Even though I felt at my lowest inside, my support team never once waivered or questioned that I would recover. They saw hope and helped me to see it.

I literally lost my identity in the September 2017 fall when my non-driver ID card disappeared underneath all of my blood in the ambulance. I had to get a new one and the picture barely looks like me. I was eager to replace my ID because the only other form of official identification I had was my passport, which I didn't want to keep carrying in my purse. I really didn't want to risk losing my passport. I waited long enough for most of the black and blue marks on my face to go down that I could cover the rest up with makeup. My face was so swollen that I could barely open my mouth to smile and I looked thirty pounds heavier.

The only tactic I could think of to try looking 'normal' was to layer on a lot of lipstick. I regret that now. My ID card photo shows me with a puffy face without a smile wearing bright red lipstick. It hurt so much to put on the lipstick, and even more to remove it when I got home.

There was a big disconnect in terms of how serious this accident was and how I was perceived. People thought that when the black and blue marks on my face went down, then I was fine. Surviving that fall was so hard and building back up felt impossible. After exactly one week, I was able to blow my nose without blood running out through the broken cavities. That was the first achievement I made since waking up in the hospital trauma ward.

Nine years of trauma came flooding back and I was in the same place again with one fall taking away everything I had worked for. Falling forward was the biggest difference between the accidents, which meant I lived through a different set of aftereffects than in 2008 when I fell backward. Fortunately, I did not fracture my skull this time and slip into a seizure coma. The immediate emergency was less life threatening, but still all too familiar.

Just like in 2008, my eyes were the first physical challenge to conquer. The sockets around both eyes and the other surrounding facial bones were so swollen that I couldn't blink for three days. Similarly, opening my mouth to breathe and to talk did not come easily. There was so much dried blood on my mouth that the nurses hadn't even been able to thoroughly clean the cuts during the first day in the trauma ward. My lips were so inflamed and covered with blood that it took almost a week before I couldn't open and close them to breathe without opening the wounds again.

The PTSD of this fall hit me so hard that I felt intense guilt for what happened. I was so overwhelmed by emotions that I had trouble putting anything into words, and crying was the only vocal response I made some days. I remember sitting in my doctor's office on a follow up visit shortly after the fall and started breaking out in tears.

"I'm so sorry," I kept apologizing to him.

He asked, "Why would you be sorry?"

"Because I feel like I just took so many steps backward after all of these years; and that it's my fault."

I couldn't get that thought out of my head. That fall was so defeating, serious, painful, and harmful to my body. After all of the progress I had made during the years from the TBI, I was back to being immobilized. This fall caused irreparable damage to my thyroid and revealed a heart condition that had never been an active issue. While I was lucky that my dentist saved the broken teeth so well, none of my teeth will ever position the same again. My smile will never beam the same as it had before. The two years of wearing braces in high school to align my teeth are futile with one fall.

On October 25, 2017, one month after the collapse, I was still sleeping in the recliner, out of my own bed, in the den to keep the back of my head from swelling.

Thirty days and counting and I still hadn't eaten any solid food. That morning, the dentist told me that my teeth were making good progress, but I needed to keep the bracket in for another month before performing a root canal. My teeth weren't up for chewing until then, but I could add overcooked soft pasta into my diet. I followed his plan and he saved my teeth enough that the broken ones are now healed and are still mine, not artificial.

After I had been recuperating for about six weeks, Kelly and I met for coffee and talked about the day of my fall in detail for the first time. She helped me piece together what happened, starting from when we met up that morning for the seminar until dropping to the pavement. She filled in the specifics from that point forward until Bob met her at the hospital. I said that I was so thankful for her help that day, but so sorry that she had to see it.

Kelly is an amazing person. She always told me never to be sorry and she was there to help me. Kelly divulged to me later how she was both impressed at how fast and responsive the paramedics were, but also how disheartened she was that people around us dispersed within seconds. She said that by the time the ambulance arrived, the handful of people who had been looming around to watch scattered, leaving her holding my bleeding body screaming and crying in her arms alone.

Kelly's description of the scene left me to wonder where the common humanity is that brings everyone together to watch a near-fatal accident, car wreck or fight, but then causes them to run away before making eye contact to help someone in pain?

Rehabilitating the second time felt very lonely. I sat and slept in a chair feeling pain, emptiness, and hopelessness. Bob's family and Kelly visited after the September 2017 fall. Friends left messages for me, but I couldn't answer their calls. I didn't have any energy. I started to feel like people were scared of me, which only reinforced that feeling to myself.

My entire family was across the country, and all I wanted to do was hug them and see their loving faces reassuring me that everything was going to be okay.

I was terrified because I didn't know when to expect the pain, headaches, inner or outer damage to my face and teeth to lessen. I couldn't use my voice to talk anymore very well, so I felt like nobody understood. I had months of rehab ahead of me before I built up my stamina again. One constant throughout was how much my Zumba® family cared for me and kept praying for my health to improve. That comfort helped take away some of my pain and give hope, which felt like magic.

I tried to jump back into my life way too soon after the 2017 fall. I was so desperate to get out of that chair and not feel so quarantined that I didn't realize until three months later I hadn't taken enough time to let my body fully recover. My stamina wasn't strong enough and as a result, I was setting myself back. I needed to take more time to rehabilitate. Since then, I've made a point to take things more slowly and not push myself until I feel healthier. I finally started listening to my body, to find out what is right for me and recognize my limits.

I'm still not one hundred percent recovered from the 2017 fall, and I don't know how long it will be until I am, or if there is a way to actually be fine. So much changed again for me that day that I am in a place where my 'new normal' might now be an 'old normal.' I can never know what will be ahead for me. Maybe my journey as a fitness instructor is changing its course or will open a new door. My stamina is not increasing on its own, which complicates being able to practice and teach fitness.

What I need to remind myself is that no matter where I am, what my injuries are, or how down I feel; I am a teacher, which is my choice and one in which I hold great pride. I realize I don't need to be standing in front of a classroom to be a teacher. I would love to teach TBI advocacy, especially since it is so true to my heart. I'm quickly learning that it might be time for something else to be part of an evolved 'new normal' and move forward. I'll keep pushing forward no matter what I endure—I'm not giving up now after working this hard.

I fought the pavement and won.

Chapter 9
My Eyes Tell My Story

My eyes tell my story in stages—my eyes define me, and that is one thing I didn't lose from the 2008 fall or 2017 fall. I own my eyes. When I was a little girl I started feeling safe, confident, and whole through my eyes. Everywhere I went, strangers would stop me and say, "Look at your eyes, you must be Nancy's daughter!" I see my eyes in my mother and aunt, especially in pictures taken of my mom before she had me.

Maybe I needed to fall on my face to wake up and see how important and valuable that tiny detail is to me. These horrific nightmares in 2008 and 2017 brought my mom and me closer together in strength and created such a specific mother-daughter bond through trauma that unfortunately, should never need to exist. Sadly, many survivors I know have been abandoned by family members after their accidents due to the amount of help and support needed for recovery.

My mom and I never considered that road as an option. My parents raised me with the same values with which they were raised—family is always first and we never abandon them, especially in time of need. The biggest difference now is that every time my mom or I call each other, the first words we say are, "Hi, nothing's wrong, everyone's all right."

I am looking at the world through black eyes and a new face. The world is also looking at me differently. I am literally a different person. I often wonder where do I go from here? I keep saying that I want to change the world and I need to believe I can. After living in San Diego for twelve years, I still don't have, or haven't carved out, a place that is mine, where I am a regular.

A place like this is important to me because it provides a sense of familiarity and a community without judgment. This habitual type of environment is something TBI survivors rely on for comfort and acceptance. I wish I could find a place for myself where I can return to mark my progression on this journey throughout the years to practice balance exercises, meditation, tai chi, or mindful breathing. Perhaps a place where I am a regular to bring a book and slowly try to read again. I lose a part of myself when I fall. But I lived through this trauma and will never let it hold me back.

What do I see when I look through these eyes—these black eyes—that are now healed? I'm empowered to give myself a third chance to make noise and use my voice as a teacher in a different way—whatever that will be.

Chapter 10
The World of Medical Challenges

Today's world presents challenges for those living with brain injuries to succeed in day-to-day activities. Honestly, I never thought about this or realized it until it affected me. Now, every day, I wake up and open my eyes feeling defensive so I can be ready to guard myself in a world that doesn't take into account the basic needs of a TBI survivor to safely live with this disability. I am certainly more aware of my actions and the surroundings I create; and it doesn't take that much extra time or effort to adapt lighting or volume in exchange for someone's safety.

I wonder who else our society ignores or doesn't consider accommodating? Imagine what a caring world we would live in, if a few more people could take a few extra seconds to remember that when waking up in the morning.

Surviving a TBI comes with a surprise bonus of becoming part of the medical world; we just skip the years of preparation and foundation. In addition to recovering and rehabilitating from a brain injury, we develop so many other complications that can require the care of multiple specialists.

I don't have a 'regular' room in one of the five hospitals—yet. I understand the pharmacology of the prescriptions I take and know the whole daytime staff at the outpatient hospital because I've been there so often, too often.

Medically, I feel like TBI survivors float in bubbles separated from everyone else. We can be left in our bubbles together, but the outside world doesn't want to bump into us because our medical conditions are different. That is true.

I would love to go to a doctor and be diagnosed with strep throat, take a prescription, and be healed in six days. It's not that black and white for a TBI survivor. It's a challenge just for a doctor to see the pain I am in, let alone be able to fix it.

The physical damage to whichever part(s) of the brain affected by the trauma are visible on an MRI, but that image is not the whole story. It's just a clue leading to uncover and treat the conditions we develop due to that specific injury. A TBI keeps eating away, slowly, at other systems in the body after the trauma. Any type of pain, disorder, or challenge to my body that is a result of the TBI is new for me, and I want to address it proactively by making an appointment with one of my many specialists right away. It's never a simple appointment with a straightforward diagnosis and prescription to fix what doesn't feel right. The obstacle to this puzzle is not the fault of either party; it's that the patient and the doctor are speaking different languages, which never makes for a good match in communication.

Trying to diagnose and treat each new issue resulting from a TBI is similar to when you drive your car to the mechanic because you hear a noise, but when you get there, the mechanic doesn't hear a noise. I walk into the doctor's office with the task of my brain processing the message from my body of what feels wrong or of concern and explaining it to the nurse. There is a pretty good chance that message will get lost in translation from the inside of my body, to my brain, and out of my mouth like in a game of telephone. By the time the doctor tries to ask me what my original problem was, I am too confused and tired to remember. Then, off I go for more lab work, returning home to wait for a phone call to learn what the next step is; all out of anyone's control.

I always refer to my TBI as the gift that keeps on giving. Still, here I am ten years later, and am just developing hypothyroidism resulting from the September 2017 fall. [13]

For some TBI survivors, the thyroid gland stops producing enough hormones necessary to keep energy levels up and running like everyone else's. [14]

This condition adds to the exhaustion I already experience every day, and to my outward appearance of lethargy and laziness. This also means that I add another medication to my growing list. Physically, I am weak because my body is trying to recover but constantly damaged. Emotionally, I spin in this cycle of up and down; sometimes hopeful that I'll recover permanently, and sometimes in total despair that I should give up trying to fight for fulfillment out of my control.

Since the start of this journey in 2008, it looks like I just sit idle, watching opportunities to challenge myself. Maybe I can get back on the track from where I started years ago, but the reality is that my brain actually hurts trying to process the simplest thoughts. I am under the care of my primary care physician, neurologist, endocrinologist, psychiatrist, physical therapist, and cardiologist. Making one appointment for any of these doctors is not a simple task. Usually I need to schedule blood work following certain doctor visits, hospital tests procedures, surgeries, pre-op visits, and follow up appointments. That is quite a lot to manage, especially while not being able to drive.

It becomes too much at one time. I want to stop this train. It's...never ending. Each time I get a phone call to schedule another test, I feel like I keep passing go without collecting any money and being sent back to the beginning to start again. One fall often leads to another fall, which can lead to more falls. I don't know how many times I've fallen. Partially because I don't remember all of them and partially because the number doesn't really matter in the big picture.

I can tell the story of my last ten years through a twenty-minute car ride in San Diego down CA-163 South and across I-8 East. I have been a patient at every hospital between Del Mar, downtown San Diego and Grossmont, and still know the Wi-Fi codes for a few. At some point along the winding road of inconclusive tests, the only way that I reach any peace is to find a balance between the medical certainties and uncertainties of living with a TBI.

The daily medical challenges become overwhelming because I feel so small in a giant sea. I go to so many doctors, appointments, and hospitals that I feel more in sync there than with my own social peers.

My body and mind keep emotionally shattering, and I keep picking up the pieces to put myself back together. I often feel alone in terms of the medical recovery because it's so hard to find anyone who can empathize with what I go through.

If someone asks me how my appointment went on a given day, the answer is always so much longer than they hoped. I attempt to explain which specialist I saw that day, why, the next step, why I don't know what is wrong with me after all of these appointments, and possibly how today's appointment is related to an accident I had ten years ago. It is reasonable for someone outside of this cycle to lose track, and interest for that matter, about any of this situation.

After this long, the medication ritual feels less personal too—leaving me as a list of prescriptions. I'm constantly undergoing physical tests, EEGs, MRIs, blood tests, and more, with each one taking a little bit of Megan away just to be analyzed. Every day for ten years, I've kept calendars of every headache, seizure, dizzy spell, medication change, and sleep abnormality in my life to be picked apart by multiple doctors.

My stamina is unpredictable because my brain is exhausted in ways unimaginable. I'm stripped of my humanity and have become a list of lab reports, tests, and scripts instead of a person. Sharing the clinical aspect of my story makes me less vulnerable—I am like any other patient.

The fear of not knowing test results, reactions to medications, if new pills will work or interact, waiting for interpretations of scans, and most of all, not knowing what each new day will bring can be never-ending. Taking my medication is a fact of my life. It's a regimen on which I am reliant and is managed by doctors.

I become so uncomfortable when people see the number of pills I take each day or overhear what medication I take. The looks of judgment are so painful, and this is another aspect of not being able to understand what living with a TBI feels like. It's hard to ask people not to treat me as if I'm a drug addict because I take the prescribed medication so I can function.

I would love not to rely on so many pills to live safely on daily basis, but that is something else out of my control.

It's also not as simple as taking a bunch of pills each day. My body needs six to eight weeks to adjust to any dosage changes and/or side effects that range from headaches, nausea, insomnia, or loss of appetite to exhaustion. These side effects directly interact with some of the conditions for which I am being treated. Since the TBI and skull fracture, I suffer from migraines, insomnia, and low energy due to hypothyroidism.

Trying to get the correct dose of each medication is not an easy task for my doctors either. Some of the pills are so strong on my system that I need regular blood tests to monitor the levels for safety. The choice for me is to take all of these pills and deal with their baggage or not take them and risk having grand mal seizures frequently. I choose to take the pills and create a safer place for me to live that brings me a little more normalcy in a world in which I already don't fit.

I live in a constant state of mystery. The times I shine are when I pull myself up from the ground. Medical tests become even more impersonal. I once wore a heart monitor for two weeks and then mailed it in a prepaid envelope hoping the little flash drive would arrive at the correct department. The data would be analyzed and results sent to my cardiologist.

All I was left with were the scrapes on my chest from where the adhesive held the electrodes to my heart with data. It's my heart, not a computer program or series of reports. My brain and heart are the two organs keeping me alive twenty-four hours per day.

One is already damaged and I sent the other one away in a prepaid envelope to Phoenix. When I finally feel like I have the upper hand on this, something else sneaks in. My stamina and metabolism are especially low since the 2017 fall, but I have a great support system, encouraging doctors and a positive attitude. While the seizures are not totally under control, the good news is that my neurologist found the right balance of medicine to lower the frequency.

A series of tests suddenly uncovered that my heart is driving the cycle of unknowns this time without receiving answers, just more pumping questions and more bloodwork. The incredibly supportive doctors who follow my case so closely and are in constant communication with me bring great comfort. They each understand why I am concerned after months of tests to not have a diagnosis, but I believe their regimen is the best for me, and I am willing to take whatever test I can on my end to help get my health on track.

I was at the cardiologist on January 26, 2018 for my third test to determine if I have a heart condition. While running on the treadmill hooked up to the EEG for the stress test, I got dizzy and fell off crashing onto the ground. Luckily, I didn't lose consciousness and knew to brace myself so I didn't land on my head. It is so defeating that after ten years, I feel like I am back to the beginning of not knowing, and not getting better.

I had a bone density test at age thirty-nine on February 2, 2018 because I am at risk for osteoporosis due to the multiple falls I've taken. I lay on a table while a giant X-ray scanned my body repeatedly. This test that is so impersonal strips away my skin, blood, and organs. While it's not invasive physically, this machine dehumanizes me in a new way—it produces 3D images of my bones. The result is another piece of paper that doesn't know me. However, I can't get the results of bone weakness out of my head because I am trying so hard to believe I can get strong.

My doctors continue to work diligently to determine what caused me to collapse and an appropriate course of treatment. I am always the regular at the blood lab. On March 1, 2018, I had more blood drawn to keep on top of my new hypothyroidism. Nearly two weeks later, I had pre-op labs drawn before being admitted to the hospital for the tilt table test the following week.

The tilt table test is to confirm if my blood pressure is, in fact, the main culprit fighting and endangering my body. There is also no guarantee this test will provide the necessary information needed to move forward, but I don't want to physically or mentally be in that place again from September 23, 2017.

During this test, I was strapped to a table, and flipped upside down forcing my blood pressure to drop so low with the goal being for me to pass out, essentially mimicking how dramatic my blood pressure may have dropped when I fell in September 2017. I was hooked up to heart monitors and my vital signs were recorded throughout the forty-five minutes of laying down and forty-five minutes of tilted at a seventy-degree angle.

They flipped me back down prone and injected a medication which radically raised my heart rate, and then I went through the test again. The dramatic flush in the volume of my heart fluids caused me to pass out while tilted up. The good news is that we finally reached a diagnosis to understand the problem with my heart, and why I collapsed in 2017. I have postural orthostatic hypotension, adding another condition to the list and another medication to the list.

Those four months felt like I was re-living the cycle of inconclusive tests from 2008 to 2010. The difference in the 2018 cycle is that I can let go of not finding an answer this time—I've learned not to let it consume me anymore. That is not how I want to live my life and spend my energy.

I stay hopeful and book every test. I follow the instructions to prepare for each exam, usually fasting for twelve to twenty-four hours before and sometimes arriving sleep deprived. I hold up my end and show up for every test, paperwork filled out, and insurance card in hand.

The bigger picture is that my doctors are all collaborative and thorough, and they dug deep enough to uncover the heart condition that caused me to collapse in September 2017. I am more educated now; more confident; less afraid and stronger. Questioning and dissecting lab reports indefinitely is not the way for me to find the solution this time. My story is not told by MRIs, blood tests, and X-rays. I tell my story. Out Loud. Unstoppable. Unfinished.

While there are certainly times that the low points in this cycle hit me, I also have learned that it is okay to feel the despair when I need to.

Feeling pain and desperation at times is human, and healthy. It is not easy to see hope as the end of the game all of the time but running from the hard times and pretending that I am not in pain does not help me when I am down. Pushing through those times and challenges, especially with support, is how I keep my head up and take the next step forward.

Chapter 11
The World of Social Challenges

The catch twenty-two of living with a TBI is that when I wake up each day, I might have full energy or zero energy, unpredictable and regardless from the prior day. In my experience, managing inconsistency is the overarching theme of social challenges for a TBI survivor. The added twist is these hurdles are invisible to non-survivors. This puzzle of instability is hard for me to handle, and even more confusing for someone who sees me participate in a fitness class, go to lunch and function normally on Tuesday, and then become overwhelmed with social anxiety and need to stay in bed all day on Wednesday.

As I've become educated during the years from my doctors and support groups, I understand that part of the answer to this puzzle is because my brain becomes so exhausted in relation to my body, which depletes how much energy my brain has before my body needs to rest.

A post-TBI world is one in which every single detail matters. Everything needs an immediate solution. I need everything to be able to happen right away and need to be able to find what I need right away. The sense of urgency is crucial because the anxiety that comes with it is what I equate with failure. I can only manage one task at a time now, and I need to complete that one task for myself. It's not about pride; it's about needing to do things on my own, and not feeling like a failure when I can't.

Living every day with a TBI is like fighting an uphill battle, losing or winning, and starting again the next day with an unknown outcome from the previous day.

When I try explaining this real-life challenge to others, so many respond, "Oh, I forget things all the time. I can never remember what I did yesterday." Someone without a brain injury who forgets daily mundane tasks is not at all in the same situation. I do not simply 'forget' details, because my brain does not always form those moments as memories. Or sometimes, I receive the most painful response, "Well that sounds kind of dramatic, don't you think?"

These are times that I truly feel alone and different. I don't like to be doubted by people who don't understand what I go through and instead make it about them rather than be supportive as I open myself up in a moment of vulnerability.

One of the environmental changes for TBI survivors that can be hard for outsiders to understand is the need to exist and function in a safe space. I feel uncertain in so many parts of my life that I crave any type of stability I can find. My safe spaces are where I will be with people who sincerely understand my condition, accept and support me through it, even on the bad days. A result of the TBI that I experience, as do some other survivors, is a combination of heightened sensitivity and failure.

At times, if someone doesn't look at me approvingly, smile when I say hello, or respond to me within minutes, I take it as a reflection on myself that I did something wrong never deserving of forgiveness. If my dog doesn't run to me when I open my arms at her, I feel rejected and that I have failed her as a parent.

This behavior might sound extreme to someone else, but it is part of my new normal. When I find a safe space with people, I hold them close. I'm terrified and paralyzed to function otherwise. I am always walking on eggshells that something I say might come out wrong from my inability to communicate well and I will no longer be wanted in that space as a direct result of my condition. I am left standing alone, in constant fear of isolation.

Scrolling through the TV guide station is too overwhelming. Forgetting to eat regularly happens. I can't pack a suitcase without having a panic attack.

Leaving the house is hard. Lights and noise are amplified to levels that my 'normal' friends don't see or hear, leaving me to feel a little more different. The social anxiety disorder I developed resulting from the TBI is crippling when it wants to be, particularly without warning. Concerts, movies, and big events using strobe lights are not accessible for people with TBIs since the erratic flashing of lights induces seizures.

Finally, ten years into my recovery and rehabilitation, I am confident asking an event host to please remove any of the lights for the safety of those in the audience with a brain injury or seizure disorder. I speak up for myself and people with TBIs to make the rooms we enter safe and inclusive for us in our new normal. It is a small step, but it is starting to raise some awareness. It's time for society to recognize brain injury the same way other disabilities are supported and accommodated for legality.

Existing post-TBI is terrifying every day. Nothing is certain even to the extent of knowing where I am to when my body or brain will shut down with exhaustion. I notice myself checking out and fading after short amounts of time on different days. Some days I have the energy to stay up for everything, while other days I only can focus for five minutes before needing to lie down and rest.

I don't know what I am missing out on when I'm not present at something because I'm not there. I make this sacrifice at the expense of not having grand mal seizures regularly, brain surgery, or more head trauma. I'll take missing events that used to be a priority so I can be alive without confusion or exhaustion. The difference now is that I don't miss whatever other people claim I am missing. I'm the only person who gets to set the value of anything for me. Looking at my life hanging from a thread gave me a chance to adjust price tags around on the values of certain parts of my life.

Just because the world right now is not ready for people with brain injuries does not mean we should stop trying to make it ours. I want to be one of many voices to help build a world that is safe for brain injury survivors as much as for those with other disabilities. The missing puzzle piece here is how low the amount of education is regarding TBIs.

I haven't worked since 2008 and I wish I could. It's still not an option with the seizures not being under control, double vision, block in communication and cognition, myriad of unknowns, and not being able to drive. Losing the ability to work for so long takes a toll on my sense of purpose and brings up a feeling of uselessness.

I was a publicist, marketing director, teacher, and counselor, but nobody asks me about being a leader and professional in that life. I took action developing a new chapter when I joined the fitness industry as a volunteer and fundraiser in the community, but sometimes I'm dismissed in that arena for not earning an income by teaching fitness.

When did I stop commanding a room? When did people stop listening to me? People stopped listening when I stopped talking with confidence.

I spent most of my career as a high school teacher and counselor. I was the person in whom children confided, who worked with them every day through their formative years and whom they sought out for comfort and assurance and guidance. I remember that part of my life and how much I loved every second of working with students. Teaching them, counseling them, celebrating their achievements and supporting them through hard times was not a job, it was part of me at my core.

Now, I am considered someone with whom people are not comfortable being around or trusting with a conversation. Now, I'm perceived as being so different that I'm not capable of imparting knowledge or counsel. This is heartbreaking and hurtful because I don't get the chance to stand up for myself. I am left with pain, heartache, and feeling as useless as being in that coma.

Living with the post-TBI anxiety disorder presents new obstacles on an inconsistent basis. I now need to deal with social anxiety. Every now and then, between a week to an hour before an event or plans with friends, I have a panic attack to the point of needing medication and having to cancel. There is no rhyme or reason why or what brings on the attacks. I would love to be with my friends and I miss that part of me who was always so social in my old normal.

The panic also sets in regarding basic planning and executive functioning skills. I need to start packing for a trip at least a week in advance, starting with the thirty- to forty-minute long choice of which suitcase to bring and for what reason. I need to start preparations for my various surroundings and any possible experiences while away for one week or one night so that I feel prepared, giving myself control over some consistency.

I start printing and organizing in a folder all of my travel documents, hotel confirmations and reservations. Still one week out, I pack my toiletries and travel pill case. I need to take a few days off to rest before starting to pack clothes. That process is so unbearable that I spend two full days literally emptying the contents of my closet onto the bedroom floor piece by piece, as I grow too overwhelmed trying to put matching outfits together.

Bob comes home to find me crying on the floor surrounded by a mess of clothes and shoes. He is always so caring and patient with me. He lifts me off the ground, puts me in bed, and brings me dinner. He picks up the clothes and puts them in a pile on the couch in the other room so I don't stress out by looking at the disorganized mess I made. The next day he sits with me to put everything back in my closet and helps me pick what to pack. This is still a few days before a trip.

A modified version of this experience occurs the night before I have any plans scheduled for the following day. Bob sits in the bedroom with me after making sure I eat dinner as I tear too many outfits out of the closet. He gathers all of the extra pieces away while I set aside the outfit to wear the following day.

Then we go through the checklist of what I need to pack in my purse: wallet with license, insurance card, cash, pills to take while I'm out, and always a handful of snacks. I pack a change of clothes and water bottle if planning for the gym. Although I never pack fear, it is always with me.

I do not know the person I am now because I fell one day, not knowing how I got here. Those days are missing from my life and I will never get them back.

The goals I spent my life working for are scrapped and I have a blank sheet of paper in front of me with nobody who understands how to read what I write. People do not talk to me because I'm different. They do not know how to communicate with me, and as a result think I'm stupid. Fear and ignorance of different ways of communication often result in judgment.

Before my accident, when I was working, my days were different and a schedule provided me with structure. The details of my day were pre-designed for me, including hours, methods of transportation, due dates for reports, and metrics for various clients. Goals were about how to best others and focused on getting a win. Now, I get to make my own choices about how I fill the details of my days. There is a separate list of responsibilities and deadlines. There is also quite a bit of freedom and a lot more creativity in the cards I hold. I have more control over why I take on the projects I do and why I get involved in what I do.

Throughout the years, I've taken on an active role in leading charity events in the community. By helping people, I also can focus on what is best for my health in the moment and overall.

I am an ambulatory adult. I can move around by myself. After my fall in 2008, the doctors weren't sure if that would be possible, but I worked hard to build my strength up and far surpassed their expectations. Nobody thought I would be walking again, let alone become a licensed Zumba® instructor with five specialties and a U-Jam Fitness® instructor.

One aspect of living with a TBI is managing daily life when many traditional types of independence are taken away. This is even true in a place like San Diego, where there is not a very strong public transportation system for a city of this magnitude. After ten years, I have learned and created ways to make this lifestyle change work for me. It is not an ideal or easy situation, but things could be much worse, so I choose to focus on finding solutions. Taxis and Uber are options; but costs can add up in the long run for someone who can't drive. Bob, his parents, and my friends have all been very generous and truly gone out of their way to assist me with transportation. Bob and Cecile re-arrange their schedules to take me to doctor appointments, tests, and social events.

My friends, especially, are so selfless that they go out of their way completely so I can join an event, a party, a fitness class, or baby shower, especially if transportation is the only thing holding back my attendance. Their generosity adds an incredible component of normalcy to my life that is constantly redefining normal, and that means so much more to me than I can ever express in words.

Carving out these ways to support my life is important and gives me hope. Finding a place to get my hair done, with a colorist I like, that I can walk to and from without becoming too exhausted is a small victory for me. I keep focusing on the fact that I am alive. Life's also not as simple, but I will figure it out because it is the independence that I have left.

For some reason, my independence doesn't feel as appreciated publicly as it is by me. If I walk outside of my condominium complex a quarter-mile right, I walk into a local center with a few casual neighborhood restaurants, our dry cleaner, ATM, flower shop, general store, and food truck.

Turning outside a quarter-mile left brings me to the trolley stop, shopping center where I get my hair done, five different places to eat, an office supply store, a bank, and a nail salon.

The gym is directly next door to me where I take my dance fitness classes with friends. The gym is also more than a fitness venue. I'm a part of their community, volunteering at fundraising events, and creating bonds of friendship. That gym is a safe space for me, and I can walk there and back home on my own whenever I want to or need to. I never feel judged. People accept me there and friends welcome me, visiting with me about parts of life beyond the brain injury. They always lend a listening ear when needed. This is also a place where I build up strength and can improve my stamina. I'm happy there and continue to befriend people who look for a break in their day to become energized, seek friendships based on inclusion and positivity, and maybe want to create a safe space of their own. Whatever the reasons, the gym brings us together instead of pushing us apart, which is something the world might benefit from so that more people will stay to help the next time someone falls.

I have many choices that I can give myself to fill my days, including taking the trolley to a few different locations where I can meet friends, and staying in on days when I don't have the energy to go out.

When I am out and about, I enjoy striking up a conversation. I tend to speak naturally and don't censor myself about having a TBI. Albeit without trying to be insulting, people often don't know the right things to say. Their words unnecessarily perpetuate the stigma of people living with TBIs.

Someone will ask me in a pitiful presumptuous tone, "What did you do today?" I start opening my mouth to respond. But before giving me the chance to speak for myself, the other person does so for me, "Oh, you probably did nothing, right?"

Many casual conversations among others begin with the question, "How was your day?"

Often people don't think to ask me how I'm doing, but that I'm not doing anything.

A phenomenon I cannot wrap my mind around is how people react when I say that I was in a coma. Most people immediately respond with, "Do you remember what it was like to be in a coma?"

There is complete disappointment that I cannot offer the rest of a science fiction thriller for which they sat on the edge of their seats through the first part of my story to them. I just told them that I lived through a near-fatal trauma and those are their first words to me? Not, "Thank goodness you survived," or, "I'm glad you are all right."

At least two dozen times, someone has said to me when finding out I don't work and am on disability, "Oh, I wish I didn't have to work like you. You're so lucky." I ask if, "[they] would rather have brain damage, a broken skull, and the responsibility to prove it instead."

Nobody responds to me. I'm okay with the conversation ending.

Another conversation I've had far too many times is being asked, "Don't you get depressed at home all day alone?"

Honestly, I don't find this to be an uplifting question.

Depending on the day, I might feel so drained that I can barely move. Other days, I might go for a walk in the nice weather or make plans with a friend. It's hard for others to know what anybody does during the day without asking.

Although not a question, the statement that hurts the most is one regarding my strength and physical appearance. Picture having an attack of vertigo and double vision while with friends and someone says, "But you look fine."

When—not if—people say this to me, I still don't have a response to give. My body is breaking down and I fight daily for my survival.

Every question someone asks me or sentence I hear is like having five thoughts to sort through and answer first in my head. How do I prove that I'm trying? Why do I need to prove it? When I look stronger or have a good day, people believe me less that my brain is sending distress signals never answered. My independence disappeared in so many ways and that is one more thing I need to fight for.

I might take some time, swings, and misses before I figure out what my next step is as a TBI survivor, but what matters is that I am trying. Those steps are coming slowly and I am making progress.

Chapter 12
A Day in the Life of a TBI Survivor

Since July 2008, I've redefined what is a 'bad day' versus a 'good day.' Before my accident, I spent so much time and energy working extremely hard to never make a mistake or disappoint anyone. My work ethic was, and still is, a strength of mine, but my priorities were misdirected. I woke up in the morning and strove toward the end goal of the week before taking my first breath. I'd spend my morning commute multitasking and planning ahead. I felt as if I needed to arrive to work an hour early and stay much later than anyone else.

I didn't need this extra time to catch up on my work, so I used it to plan every step of the week ahead in each capacity I served, read over every piece of communication for the third time, started on upcoming tasks, and never stopped to take even one second to enjoy my days. This continuous ambition had me so wound up and looking in the wrong direction. If I didn't schedule every passing minute with productivity, I felt a constant race against the clock that I was failing and not doing enough work-related activities. Any type of delay would bring all of these plans crashing down, and I didn't have the extra time to start over. A scheduling delay used to define a 'bad day' for me.

A tragedy certainly changes perspective. Recovering from a TBI means to wake up in a world without a schedule, or one that needs to allow for flexibility. I stopped focusing on productivity, running late or not doing enough work. Instead, I take a long deep breath when I wake up and am thankful to be alive. If I have the energy to check something off the to-do list, that's great. If not, then it can wait until the next day. A good day is a day that I wake up. It's much easier to decipher between the bad days versus good days, with a lot less criteria.

A bad day for a TBI survivor feels like torture. I wake up not knowing where I am, what day it is, or feeling any familiarity of my surroundings—in my own home. I need to stay in my pajamas because putting an outfit together makes my heart race and body fill with anxiety just to get dressed. I swallow my morning pills because I know I won't be able to function otherwise—and it's not looking uphill from here.

At this point, I slowly and cautiously make my way to the kitchen, constantly being afraid of falling. I make a cup of coffee, with the noise from the Keurig ringing like a rocket taking off in my ears. I will either drink the coffee sitting on the couch next to my dog, Emmie, or bring her back to bed. In either case, it feels like I just finished three days of activity.

When Bob leaves for work I am home alone with our dog by myself, and I am terrified. I have difficulty taking care of myself on a daily basis, let alone feeding and walking Emmie enough for exercise. I never remember to administer her daily pills—I don't even know what medicine she takes. I'm afraid that I'll break her when I put her back in bed with me. Emmie, is less active than I, but the responsibility of caring for her scares me.

Emmie came into our lives at just the right time, from just the right person. When Bob and I moved into our building in San Diego in 2006, we met Anita Hunter. She lived upstairs from us and owned two dogs: Emmie and Harley. We joked that Bob and I were the dogs' godparents. When taking the dogs out for their daily walks, Anita would often knock on our door asking if we wanted to join them. During these daily outings, Anita and I grew to know each other very well. Not only is she a professor with a Ph.D. in Educational Leadership, but she is also a nurse practitioner. Bob and I were so thankful for her expertise as a healthcare professional and her encouragement as a friend.

After I started walking around the neighborhood more, Anita brought Emmie to visit every few days since she was so quiet and wouldn't jump or run around. I sat on the couch petting Emmie's beautiful brown and white coat feeling so relaxed.

I joined them for more walks and Anita made sure to give me Emmie's leash, so I could start gaining back my balance and self-confidence. Anita's plan worked. We went for short, five-minute walks at first. After a few weeks, I was on track for slightly longer walks including climbing up and down the stairs.

A few years later, Anita moved north of San Francisco to be closer to her family. Bob and I went upstairs for our final visit to wish her safe travels and give her our love. While reminiscing and shedding some tears together, Anita asked us if we wanted to become Emmie's parents instead of godparents. She saw how attached Emmie was to us and how much we loved her. We were honored at this thoughtful and selfless gesture, but worried that Anita would miss Emmie too much.

Anita also didn't think the dogs would be upset by being separated. Her instincts were right as she hit the nail on the head. Anita tells me that Harley calmed down a lot because he isn't competing for her attention anymore. Emmie has just thrived now that she is the 'Queen Bee' in our household and doesn't need to compete for attention. Emmie is more active, animated and social than ever before. She stays at home with me during the days and follows me into whichever room I settle for most of the day.

Bob and I thought that separating the dogs would be too hard for them, but Anita assured us that she was confident in this choice, especially because Emmie was still helping me recover and regain my balance. Her calm demeanor is a perfect fit for me as there are days that my head is filled with so much noise that putting one sentence together is beyond overwhelming.

Part of the curse of living with a TBI is being trapped inside my own mind eternally. Writing my thoughts down doesn't help, crying makes the pain worse, and talking about it raises the frustration because those same thoughts still don't come out with any clarity. Then I just give up, which is the worst feeling.

It takes time for me to adjust to change. I wish I was all better and could live in the positive all the time, but that is not a choice I get to make.

The good comes with the bad, and I want the good. The new version of myself has very different needs than the old me. I need more rest. I need more time to form thoughts into words. I need more time to complete seemingly simple tasks. In addition, I need my loved ones to realize and be patient with the fact that my emotions are so much harder to manage than they used to be.[15]

Different feelings come in ebbs and flows. The days when I feel strong and confident are the ones that I know are best to take an exercise class, have lunch with friends, work on a project at home, attack a few items on my to-do list, respond to emails and phone calls, and enjoy feeling happy. This handful of things might be ordinary daily tasks for others, but for me when I accomplish these things, I experience great victory, especially when I feel like an underdog in life.

There are days I don't feel confident, but at the same time I don't feel like the day is impossible. On these days, I wake up while Bob is still home before leaving for work. His presence helps me understand where I am and that I can get out of bed. He reminds me to take my pills, which removes the stress of needing to make that decision myself. At that point, I am awake and feel confident enough to function that I turn on my computer and bring it to the bedroom to check email before getting dressed. I still need to handle the anxiety that will come with choosing an outfit and getting dressed.

Even though I change out of my pajamas, I have used enough energy at that point so I take a late morning nap. The rest of the day follows a similar cycle, doing some volunteer work on the computer, walking Emmie, talking with my mom on the phone, another nap, and sometimes I will take an exercise class. This is a very good day for me.

The days when I feel overwhelmed and filled with anxiety terrify me. My heart races so fast that I can't move. My body is paralyzed with fear. The most upsetting part is that I no longer have the ability to articulate why this apprehension takes over. My brain and body are just exhausted, and I can't function from the second I awaken through the state of panic that renders me worthless for the rest of the day.

I work to turn a bad day into a good one. I spend my energy embracing my cheerleaders and letting go of the extra noise. I've had two very narrow escapes, so I am hyper aware to live a life of compassion and forgiveness. For me, survival is living in a non-stop cycle of periods of vulnerability turning over my body and mind to so many doctors, and then periods of empowerment and strength that I must hold close to keep hope that my condition will improve.

The scary part is that the cycle doesn't have a consistent pattern and I don't have any control over it. I know to celebrate those moments of strength because I never know how many more are ahead. As a TBI survivor, sadly those moments don't last long.

On July 10, 2010, two years to the date of my first fall, I had another grand mal seizure in an exercise class with friends and woke up in the ambulance en route to the hospital. Bob met us there, and he, along with my three friends from the class, refused to leave my side.

Shortly after being released home, we realized it would be smart to get a medical bracelet on the chance that I have an accident in front of people who I don't know. Thank goodness, we did so, because I've had so many additional falls and seizures since that day, paramedics tell me that having the information on the bracelet has saved my life. That bracelet is only one of the first steps to finding my lost identity. I actually put that bracelet on for the first time two years after my first accident.

As cliché as it is, I developed a new appreciation for life after the fall in 2008 and was reminded of what I almost lost again in 2017. I used to be so smart and thrived on intellectual challenge. I miss that so much.

I cannot believe how exhausting it is just to write a few sentences that make a modicum of sense together. I miss being able to organize my thoughts quickly. I remember copy editing and writing press releases while walking down the street. Now I need at least eight hours to write 1,000 words. Writing with a pen and paper feels so defeating because I cannot spell correctly anymore. These are facts that I accept because I need to grab life and run while I have the chance.

I have the power to redefine my standards of perfection and success. I also am the one who can reframe my perception of a challenge to be a vehicle for change and opportunity to rise. This is also a time when I have reframed what fear means to me. I fear what I can lose—my life, my husband, my family and friends. I am not afraid of what other people think of me or if they may be disrespectful. That is not the fear that matters in the end. I choose to spend the energy I have being positive and hopeful, not engaging in toxicity and despair.

Things are different for TBI survivors. We look at everything in front of us, including questions asked of us, through a different lens. The question, "What would you do if today was the last day of your life?" has a separate meaning for someone who came face-to-face with that inquiry. I've pondered this frequently throughout the years, especially when new milestones pass or my health status changes. This is really two separate questions in reality, which poses two answers.

1) What would you do if today was the last day of your life, and you didn't know it?
2) What would you do if today was the last day of your life, and you knew it?

Answering the first is much easier for me, as I have been there and honestly not discovered anything newly profound about myself. If I woke up on a regular morning, not knowing it would be my last, I would go about my typical day. I tell the people in my life how much I care about them all the time; we don't need to wait until a dramatic last breath to confirm that we care about each other. I am not putting off doing something fun or working for a goal out of fear. Perhaps I did in the past, but after experiencing how quickly it can all be gone, I let go of being so rigid so I can enjoy my life.

The second question is harder to deal with. I don't know how dramatic I would choose to live that twenty-four hours compared to enjoying my life as much as in a typical day. I would probably eat more of a decadent breakfast of blueberry pancakes and chocolate chip pancakes, with no protein, and a muffin on the side.

I would probably indulge in a few things similar, but I don't know that I would make any grand sweeping gestures or statements that I felt the need to say before I died. I don't live my life holding that type of regret inside or feeling as though I've made the wrong choices.

I am the only person who can control my choices and the way I respond to any given situation. There are times I question if I fought hard enough during these years. Maybe I spent too many days not getting out of bed or not trying to push my energy ahead. Sometimes I sit here wondering if I could have fought harder for myself, and then I take a step back and give myself a break for not finding answers to the past. The truth is that I did fight as hard as I could on any given day, and still do. I don't consider myself weak because I have a TBI. I am strong because I am living with a TBI, and I am the one who sets the perception for my own life.

Chapter 13
TBI is an Invisible Disability

A traumatic brain injury is an 'invisible disability' because people who look at me can't see the damage on my brain and can't see what challenges I face every day, which makes raising awareness and support so difficult.

People can't see how debilitating a TBI is to every aspect of life, especially that I might or might not lose consciousness at any moment.

I have the responsibility to prove to other people that I have a disability, even though I 'look normal.' We are trying to thrive in a world that is not patient enough to understand how we are different and why this disability is invisible.

If I broke my leg in that same room with the bone protruding and blood gushing on the floor, anyone would call 911 immediately and comfort the person in pain. Instead, people just stare at me.

This amount of work is so draining emotionally and physically, that it makes it even harder to function successfully. With the impaired cognition and retention challenges, people often treat me as though I have a learning disability or attention-deficit hyperactivity disorder (ADHD) instead of engaging in a discussion with me to understand what is really happening. I refuse to let any of this keep me down.

While I understand that people just want to help me, I wish that they would ask how they can help or what I need. I don't have a learning disability, so providing that treatment will not help me.

I take twenty-seven pills daily. This number is one more way that I'm identified as a walking medical chart and less of a person with each new prescription. I need almost an hour to fill up my weekly pill boxes, which I do for two weeks at a time.

Bob sits with me to help in case I miss one or have an anxiety attack from the magnitude of the task. I feel discouraged week after week, year after year, completing my Saturday night pillbox regimen, but I know that if I don't set the time aside for it, I will put myself in danger of missing doses.

The responsibility is on us to make our new environment a place to function safely. Specific handicap accessibility doesn't exist for TBI survivors. Providing for this invisible disability means that we either make accommodations or leave. People give dirty looks when I use the accessible seats on trolleys and buses.

I get nasty glares when I use the wheelchair at the airport. More than once, flight attendants have asked me why I need a chair or what is wrong with me. I point to my medical bracelet and say, "I have a traumatic brain injury and seizure disorder."

I still find it unbelievable that people with TBIs need to prove their disability. When someone says they have a well-known health condition people accept it. I have not witnessed anyone question to see their medical records, blood tests or prescription lists. I am living with an invisible disability and it gets frustrating.

I need to educate each of my friends so they know how to save my life if needed. We do not learn how to help someone having a seizure during CPR classes. As a fitness instructor and classroom teacher, I never learned how to help someone with a TBI in case of emergency. Educating those closest to me has been the hardest. They have seen me as strong and don't want to accept me as weak.

Through human nature, we rely on and trust what we can see and what is familiar. With a brain injury, we can't see it and nothing is familiar about it.

What a survivor needs to understand is that living with this disability is overwhelming enough, and a separate list of questions follows their loved ones, caregivers, and then strangers.

What is important for people to understand about brain injuries is they are severe traumas. Having a scar on the back of my head does not make my injury any less tangible than someone who is in a body cast or a wheelchair. The difference is the visibility, which creates familiarity.

But one reality exists: only someone who lives with a TBI understands what it feels like to live with a TBI. Other people can only give so much sincere sympathy but can never give empathy. There is a large community of TBI survivors with whom I have been able to connect. Speaking with other survivors are the only times I engage in a natural conversation about my daily life with a TBI.

We talk about how we got our TBIs, the various resulting medical conditions we live with, how our families and friends respond to us, who at the table has the worst time management, and what we did in our old normal. We compare the medications we take and laugh about the awful side effects from some.

I exist in my old normal with these comrades. Conversations with close friends and family members in my new normal feel censored regarding the TBI. Rarely do other people bring it up, and if they do so, it's in a quiet voice with delicacy, mimicking a fear that I might break emotionally. I always say that I am happy to talk about my TBI because it is part of me. I don't pretend it's not there and I'm not ashamed or embarrassed to be a survivor of a near-fatal trauma.

Living with a TBI is not as black and white as it might appear. There are no simple solutions or automatic systems in place to make life a little more manageable. While most of us lose our drivers' licenses, each of us has to meet a different set of criteria to qualify for the reduced disability public transit rate. While returning to work is not possible right away for many survivors, the disability approval process is long and not standardized for a TBI disability.

For me, it is an emotional and physically draining process, not to mention a lengthy one, waiting for the response to arrive at least one month later. Filling out these forms drudges up the minutia of the past years and it also inhibits any concept of recovery I try to make.

I feel as if I am taking steps backwards. It's a huge challenge cognitively to write the answers in the forms, and Bob is wonderful to help, but I wish he didn't need to.

Each new adventure, big or small, comes with a new set of accommodations I need in order to be successful. This is an area where my old normal rears its head, as troubleshooting and brainstorming have always been my areas of strength. Creating new avenues and modifications for living with a TBI is a work in progress that I've built up throughout the past decade.

A key factor for my success is the self-care my body and brain need when I have a bad or tired day. I don't wallow in a feeling of failure or ask why I don't feel capable to take on the world the same way as the day before. I rest and reset for the next day, understanding that it's okay to take a break in my new normal, and it would have been okay to take breaks in my old normal too.

Taking a look from an outsider's perspective at the brain injury culture, it might appear small, but it's not. I think people forget that each brain injury is different, which puts each survivor on different timelines in their recoveries. Not everyone is ready at the same time, nor do they always want to talk about or share their experience in the same manner for any number of reasons.

Some survivors speak publicly to large audiences, some speak to smaller groups, some write books, some write blogs, and others often lead local support groups and/or online support groups only for the brain injury community to create a safe space of support.

Unfortunately, it's common for brain injury survivors to undergo bullying, name-calling, and other negative behaviors from peers and family members who prejudge them based on stigmas instead of listening to their stories.

This is also important because raising awareness and fundraising is not a responsibility that should land only on the shoulders of survivors. This is a worldwide disability, which makes it the responsibility of the entire community to work together for the same goal. This begs the question of why does the responsibility of brain injury awareness fall only on brain injury survivors, thereby isolating us even more socially?

I have a full life that is just different from the life I had ten years ago. I accept my physical and mental limitations as I learn them. With that acceptance comes initial frustration and a craving for resolution to do everything. Then I sit back and reframe that I can be one hundred percent present at the events I attend and where I volunteer.

There are times I feel helpless and I admit that is okay—admitting that I am not alone in this journey is a powerful attribute. It doesn't make me weak, it makes me human. Writing and reading exhaust my brain in ways they never did, and in ways, I fear never will come back. This is a real injury, and I appreciate that it is difficult to truly understand.

I've embraced the challenge of increasing TBI advocacy in my community. I volunteer with the San Diego Brain Injury Foundation as a mentor to new survivors. Winter 2018 marked the first time I led my own team to raise money for the foundation's surviveHEADSTRONG - Walk for Brain Injury Recovery.

Five friends joined my team, "Walk Strong with Megan." I decided to take on the challenge of leading my own team rather than just signing up to walk because I want to be a voice for brain injury awareness. Everything leading up to the walk took place online.

The foundation made it simple to register a team and create the team fundraising page. With social media, email, and the power of word-of-mouth, I began to engage people in conversation about the walk and then send them information to join the team.

The night before the walk I logged onto our team site and was filled with warmth at the generosity of people whose donations actually sent us right over the fundraising goal with a total of $1,100.

The 2-mile walk along Mission Bay didn't appear to be difficult, but it was going to be cold. The morning of the walk on March 10, 2018, was overcast and a little misty. I hoped that the SDBIF wouldn't cancel the event. I sent messages to our team reminding them to wear layers and bring hats because of the wind. I often walk at Mission Bay and whether cold or hot, windy or not, the bay is a peaceful place to get away.

Located only a few miles from downtown San Diego, the bay is lined with palm trees, trails for walking or exercising, and plenty of benches to sit and enjoy the calm waters. It was the perfect place for the surviveHEADSTRONG - Walk for Brain Injury Recovery.

Team members planned to meet behind the registration tent at 8:15 a.m. I called the foundation a week prior to find out the color of the event T-shirts. I wanted to give everyone on our team a matching bandana to help unify us, build some team spirit, and have a 'prop' for photos.

The blue bandanas also made it easy for team members to find each other by waving them in the air. The five of us found each other quickly by waiving the bandanas and making a few phone calls of, "Okay, keep walking straight. I'm waving at you. Turn your head right-no, the other way. I'm in front of you."

I had the chance to introduce everyone to the director of the foundation and give her a bandana as well. We took fun photos with our blue T-shirts on over the layers and raincoats we wore. Between the registration tent and start line was a large vendor area plus tables with breakfast and bottled water.

At 9:00 a.m. sharp, an announcement was made to warm up. The crowd gathered for a light stretch to warm up our bodies in the cold damp weather. Then it was time to walk for brain injury awareness.

Walking those two miles with my team meant everything to me. Participants, family, and friends came out to walk two miles in the shoes of a traumatic brain injury survivor. During the stretch, two of my friends said, "We need to make this huge next year and get a really big team out here."

"Walk Strong with Megan" brought hope that I am not one voice alone trying to make a difference. Their statement brought me hope that we are more than five voices.

I was honored by their support, generosity, and warmth with which they brightened the day. The most amazing part of leading that team was watching everyone rally together and instantly become so passionate about advocacy for brain awareness. They started brainstorming and committed to building a larger team for the walk next year. The small steps make a difference when we take them together.

In addition to volunteering for the San Diego Brain Injury Foundation, I also communicate with leaders at U-Jam Fitness® and Zumba® for advice to grow as an advocate, and I am thankful for their faith in me and constant support.

Becoming a part of my local TBI community is such an empowering and active step that I've taken. I'm doing my part in raising the level of discourse about TBIs in a constructive way, as much as I can. While it can be impossible to get over the trauma or forget it, it is possible to move out of the past to give myself a future.

Chapter 14
How to Support TBI Survivors

With every TBI being different, every survivor has different needs for their recovery process. What works for me might not work well or effectively for another, however, there are some things I've found to be in common from discussions with other survivors.

Before anything else, please surround TBI survivors in a non-judgmental environment in order to heal.[16] I feel like I am being looked at under a microscope while people wait to watch my behavior. It's emotionally overwhelming and draining to wonder if I'm being watched or judged.

Communication is a tremendous challenge for TBI survivors. One of the hardest, most difficult times is when I can't express what kind of pain I'm in, or type of help I need. Each day is different in my head, and I need support where I am at any given moment, not in the past and not what might come next. It's hard for me to live in the present because my present keeps changing a few steps ahead, without giving me a map of how to keep up.

Communication is important on a larger scale to help educate others about the myths of brain injuries and stereotypes of those with brain damage. This lack of understanding could very well be the reason that someone feels uncomfortable talking about brain injuries.

Survivors want to explain what our condition is, and the way to get there is by knowing there will be listening ears on the other side of the conversation when we share our story.

The greatest support mechanism that I need to manage my TBI on a daily basis is patience. Now, ten years later, my entire life is still a place I don't understand, and it is new every morning. I still need time to find my footing, and I need even more time to communicate with other people from a new point of view every twenty-four hours.

Patience is also something important for other people in my life to accept regarding the new requirements and adjustments my mind and body need to recover. One of the changes to which I am still adapting is that I need more rest than I did before the TBI, and my stamina changes from day to day. I want to push myself the way I used to.

I feel discouraged when I burn through a ninety-minute fitness class, and I need to sleep for the following six hours. There is a limit that I can reach physically on a daily basis—because the source of energy from my brain gets depleted and I need to rest, and sometimes that means I need to sit or lie down—but that doesn't mean I don't want to try to work harder. I always want to work harder. I came way too far and fought way too hard to give up on myself.

The fear of being alone is frequently on my mind. There are still times, however, that I am afraid that I will be judged, or given up on, when I can't keep up, need to cancel plans, can't remember things, can't communicate clearly, can't walk without bumping into people, can't function without specific step-by-step instructions, or when I am overwhelmed by something that is basic to everyone else. Instructions and simplicity help me feel normal. Otherwise, I would be swallowed up at times. I know I am asking for a lot of patience from people, especially regarding communication, but I am working very hard to communicate. Deep inside, I am scared that people will run out of patience and walk away from me.

I am incredibly grateful for my family and friends who have taken the time to learn how I need to communicate in my new normal and asked how to best communicate with me. The wiring inside my brain changed in 2008, and it hasn't been fixed yet. Even though I have difficulty conveying my words at times, I still can add value to the conversation and I want to.

Education is such a big topic in the brain injury world, so much so because we need more of it. There is nothing wrong with not automatically understanding everything about a TBI, so learning about brain injuries can be a great way to support those with TBIs and to spread awareness. I always appreciate the opportunity to explain my life in my own words, not through other perceptions or misinformation about TBIs. I am the first one who wants to provide clarity about brain injuries and am honored to have the chance to advocate.

The next step is for my support team, those who listen during conversations and learn, those who never realized how big TBIs are to stand and advocate with me, and with other survivors. Spreading the education is more powerful with more voices. TBI survivors can't do this alone because it's too draining. We are spreading the message, now it's time for the rest of the community to help.

Most importantly, I don't want to be treated differently. I am a person before I am a patient. I accept the deficits that I work very hard to compensate for as much as possible. There is never a reason to take pity on me or feel sorry for me. I don't take pity on myself or feel sorry for the life that I live.

Something that gets overlooked is the manner in which people communicate with a survivor. To support us, be sure that you are speaking to us and including us in the conversations. It is hard for me to feel empowered when I'm being ignored while people talk about me instead of with me. Be compassionate and realize the weight of comments made when speaking with a survivor.

When someone finds out that I have a brain injury, the response is always, "Oh, how awful, you poor thing." I feel total confusion by that comment and I think that it is a little intrusive for someone to assume my life is awful and try to shame me. I take pride for being triumphant over all of these years.

I am taking advantage to live my life fully, with happiness and no regrets. I entered the hospital in 2008 and I was alive—just barely, but my body was ready to fight and not give up.

I can't give up on myself. I don't want to feel like a sick person all of the time just because I have a bad day. Being treated that way certainly makes my good days feel less like celebrations.

From grammar school through college, I was one of the 'smart kids,' which made me proud. I worked hard and developed a true love of learning, reading and critical thinking. After ten years, I am still working hard through my recovery as a TBI survivor. While I am very grateful for my positive outcomes and growing strength, this is the first time that no matter how hard I work, I don't feel like one of the 'smart kids.'

The cognition, focus, recollection, and analytical skills have not returned. I believe that the accident in 2008 and the mental and physical challenges I deal with are meant to be part of my destiny as I evolve and allow for me to serve others in new ways. I don't dwell on my deficits. Since that accident, I wake up each morning with gratitude for my family, friends, health, and anything that brings me a smile.

Part of life for someone living with a brain injury is often a specific medication plan that is quite personal. One thing to keep in mind is just because we are comfortable sharing our stories, we might not want to discuss our medication. That aspect should be in the hands of the survivor and not pushed. When I get asked about the many anti-seizure and anticonvulsant prescriptions I take, I feel uncomfortable because of the negative stigmas associated with some of these. I take strong medications that include controlled substances. I am educated about each of my pills, but I do not want to share that information with someone who I don't know or who doesn't have a full understanding of each pill.

TBI survivors rely on those who can cheer on their victories, of all sizes. I often don't feel a sense of purpose every day, which can feel emotionally defeating. In my old normal, I was strong at work, ambitious, productive, active, organized, and incredibly extroverted. This isn't the case anymore. I have a sense of purpose when I can accomplish just one task that I would not have blinked at before.

The support from loved ones also gives me back my sense of purpose. Bob is aware of how much this change still affects me. Every day he looks at me while I am doing something and says he is proud of me. Those few little words mean so much to me because I know that I am not building back up alone, and I am gaining a new sense of purpose.

Bob is not the only person who keeps my spirits up in this way. My mom believes in me and tells me she is equally proud of my progress. My mother is beautiful. We both have blonde hair; however, she stands just an inch shorter than me at 5'3" with a smaller frame. She always wears a perfectly-matched golf outfit or daytime Capri sets. She is in great shape from a combination of gym workouts, yoga, or daily four-mile walks. This makes her look as strong on the outside as she is on the inside.

My mom always touches her index finger to her nose when she is concentrating on something or deep in thought. It sends the message to anyone around her that she is in a mindful state of focus and will not absorb any outside noise. A few years ago, Bob caught me mimicking the same such behavior. I never realized that I followed suit, until now. Mom and I both answer the phone in the same way with the same serious tone, "Hi. What's going on?" Then we break out laughing because we are calling about something silly like trying to remember the name of a song.

I love to see mom's big smile. She radiates joy when she laughs, which is often. She is easy going with her friends and family, and I love that she is confident and fun-loving. My mom is an amazing role model, and I want to emulate her and the love she shows every day for her family and friends.

The memory of my father always lifts my spirits. I often wonder what my life would be like if my dad was still alive in 2008. When I remember his sincere support, I know he was, and still is, with me. And this keeps me going. While most days are good days, the reality is that some days do feel hopeless and I wonder if I will ever regain the capacity to move forward from where I am right now. I wake up and often don't know what day it is. Getting dressed brings on anxiety.

It's been hard to find my limits mentally and physically, but I try to listen to my body. The truth is that I don't know what lies ahead for me, which is something I have gotten used to, and actually use as a reminder to enjoy these days.

When I open my eyes in the morning, I try to see the world as achievable, and I need to keep seeing it as so, which I can't do alone. I believe that I have the power to own my choices and be a source of positivity and strength as a result. I am excited, determined and confident to ask for help when I need support. Surrounding myself with good people helps me radiate positivity. There are those in my life who understand this condition, are patient and compassionate with me, and I am so grateful for them.

Chapter 15
Survivor Choices

As a TBI survivor, I've made a lot of choices during the years. Some are small choices, while others are the choices about how to approach life and how to go forward with true purpose. In 2008, I needed to start over and think about what type of professional life and identity I would have. Unable to see into the future doesn't allow me to know how long my recovery will continue, what unknowns will come my way, or what else I might discover throughout this journey.

To thrive in the new normal means accepting the deficits while still maintaining values and passion. I still want to fight to maintain a love of learning. I miss reading novels, short stories and works of non-fiction. I have tried but I can't maintain the retention and concentration long enough to go from one page to the next. I have tried listening to audio books, but they are even harder for me because there is nothing tangible to hold. It's just a voice in the middle of the room with nothing on which to focus. I've progressed throughout the years to the point that I can now read and understand longer articles that jump to another page. It's just not the same. I used to devour books. I loved the feel of a paperback in my hand and smell of the pages. There was a feeling of how much the author poured their soul into it, and then that story becomes part of my soul.

I still get discouraged when I can't communicate well enough to say 'thank you' to my family, or apologize to someone when I am confused, or tell a friend why their support is so important to me.

When I feel tired or lack energy, I get under the covers and take a nap until my brain has the energy to restart again. I own my choice to nap instead of being self-destructive.

I have never felt anger about the TBI; only hope, faith, and fear. I'm not a victim, but I'm living a life, one that I didn't get to choose. I'm scared of wasting my days because I fought so hard to live. My body defied the odds and doctors and keeps doing it. The world has tried to stop me twice, but God and I have different plans. My brain injury is a part of me.

Unlike other conditions through which a surgeon removes a portion of the body, I didn't have one part of me taken. That distinction is important to me. My body fought so hard to keep me that the whole brain bleed reabsorbed onto my temporal lobe so the neurosurgeon didn't even have a chance to remove it.

I work hard and I don't enter into anything lightly. At every place I worked and for every volunteer event I entered, I put in long hours, training, doing grunt work, and helping with more than anyone asked. I wanted to be good at my job and my industry as I grew into my career. That last step never happened. Time ran out for me to grow into my career as an educator at twenty-nine years old. All of the time, work and energy I focused toward my future plans evaporated when I hit the library floor in 2008.

My future wasn't gone because my life changed. I started over and worked from the ground up in the fitness industry. This was a huge undertaking for someone with no fitness or dance background and coordination deficits from a TBI. By this point, I can't compare my timeline to my friends' careers.

They are all ten years ahead of me in the workforce, and I am back at year one again in a new industry at entry level. I never became the veteran, seasoned teacher I always saw down the road. Piecing my identity together feels impossible sometimes when I don't know which parts fit in the puzzle. I remind myself that new puzzle pieces don't exist yet, as there are parts that could enter my world tomorrow.

A momentary short circuit in the brain holds the power to make one life disappear and bring a new one in to take over without warning. I remember the old life but know it's not coming back. I know I will never cross that line again to 'before.' I live in a constant state of 'after.' Then a choice presents itself—to live the new life fully without holding back, or to give up. What follows the second choice is a much shorter story with a lot less drama.

When I have a hard day, I take it ten minutes at a time, breathe, reset, and start the next ten minutes. I acknowledge myself for conquering those prior ten minutes. It's more manageable to take on the world in smaller pieces.

I'm also not spending my energy on comparing myself to other people and measuring my success and happiness against anyone else's. My perception of achievement is not marked by objects, awards, or money. Those inanimate objects wouldn't separate me apart from a crowd. My heart, integrity, compassion, and making an impact on just one person are what separates me as an individual.

When I succeed at something I've been told people don't think I can do, I build up hope that I can do more and surpass more goals than I ever thought possible. Excelling at something that nobody thought I'd be able to as a TBI survivor is actually the first time I finally believe in my own potential to succeed. I'm seeing what my parents, family, friends, and Bob see in me.

I am a problem solver and troubleshooter; those are skills from my old normal that I apply each day to this ongoing journey. I work hard to win the battles and the wars, because they are not independent of each other. I need to slay the smaller dragons step by step by step so I can rest and take a break. Only then will I have earned the necessary tools and energy to approach the bigger dragons with force and confidence.

I go to bed each night and wake up the next day with the choice to stay in bed or to stand up. Making that choice is the first one toward not being a victim. I decide to take my medication, but I own that step in the right direction.

There are days I want to get out of my pajamas and some that I don't, but I'm okay with that. My next choice is always to walk to the coffee machine in the kitchen even if I fall en route; I will still make it there. Those few choices that are so minor and such insignificant aspects to anyone else's day, exhaust me for the next hour.

I lived through these traumas but I do not let them hold me back, and I never will. I do not always know which road to choose because there are often roads not built until I get there—I need to change things by creating new paths and plans. There is not just one mold for a conqueror.

I will not give up on my life. When I stop dreaming and stop trying, that is the moment I start taking life for granted. I do not believe in defeat—telling me that I should stop makes me push harder. Telling me that I can't do something lights a fire so I push harder to prove I can. I keep pushing to educate about the capabilities of TBI survivors—not just for one day, but for the long term.

My determination and resilience did not decline between my old and new normal. These are the values that I leaned on when I felt too hopeless, too much pain, and too much despair; and then I got through. I pushed through the pain, clawed the darkness, and pulled my support team in tightly when they took my hand and led me toward hope.

It is okay to work at moving forward and see the possibilities ahead beyond being a patient. TBI survivors are not the only survivors out there, and the future is limitless not limited.

Chapter 16
Survivor Guilt

Surviving a trauma is a lot to process. To survive with a quality of life physically and mentally better than expected is overwhelming. I am grateful and thankful for my outcomes and progress. I accept my deficits and adapt my life, because I am always aware that everything could have been harder for me, or that I might not have survived any of these falls. That is actually a different kind of pain, and the most personal pain therein lies.

The pain sitting deep inside my stomach surrounded by walls is survivor guilt—always having the weight on my shoulders of the work I leave on my loved ones, who never say one word when I am too hard to handle. I have my difficult days and my breaking points, and I know they must have theirs, but they don't ever let me know. It's guilt for the silent selflessness of their burden to make my life worth living.

When I got home from the hospital in 2008, not only did everything change for me, but everything changed for Bob, my mom, Stephen, Cecile, Don and so many family and friends. I'm grateful for Bob's support, especially as he picked up another full-time job. I never want to be perceived as asking for too much or expecting anything. I am so thankful, but they don't ask for a break.

What I feel most guilty about is that he remembers every detail of the ten days I will never know. When he watches me struggle, I see his eyes relive those days in a flash. He will never be able to wipe away what he saw, heard, and experienced from his mind, while I will never be able to share that pain with him, or help take any of it away.

It can't be easy to have the amount of patience and be so willingly flexible for anyone to accommodate for me. It touches my heart that my family members and friends are so generous to adjusting their own lives without question, for a condition they do not have.

I'm aware that the top hits on my running soundtrack are:
- "I'm trying as hard as I can and following the directions from the doctors."
- "I'm resting a lot so that I don't have a setback."
- "What day is it?" "Where am I supposed to be?"
- "I don't think that I ate anything today."

It must be hard for my loved ones to hear these statements for a decade, in addition to keeping silent and supporting me each time I repeat these unforgettable classics.

There are the times I don't want to share with Bob or my mom. At times, I give up on me, but never want to be an extra burden or further disappointment than I feel like I already am. My biggest fear is that everyone will give up on me and walk away for good, as some others already have.

I've accepted the many parts of living with a TBI and understanding that it's not my fault. It's a part of my life now and I have many opportunities ahead. I spend a lot of time learning about the condition, advocating and growing awareness in the community, participating in charity events and hosting fundraisers.

These past ten years have not been a void of wasted time, but it does not get easier when I think about why I survived when others do not. I never feel like I am doing enough as a survivor. I carry guilt as someone who has lived through two major head traumas in ten years. I don't know why I deserve to be saved.

I keep asking myself, "What am I supposed to do with my life now?" That question haunts me as loudly today as it did ten years ago.

I hope to one day know the answer, but maybe I won't. I haven't given up on seeking out what my calling is in my new normal because I am meant to do something other than teach high school. I want to help change the perception that people with disabilities are limited and make an impact in the current culture to be more inclusive instead of isolating people with disabilities.

I never thought about the idea of belonging before my 2008 fall. Now, I think about it all the time. Looking back, I never realized that I took for granted the comfort and ease of being part of different social groups. There were groups of people from work, from a gym or workout classes, church, the 'spouse and date' friends, and from various social activities. Belonging in a group is about people wanting you to be with them because you have something in common automatically.

Since 2008, I don't automatically have a community of which I am a part. I can't work, so other friends do things after work together without me. I don't have the stamina to keep up at the gym or take all the classes, so I am solo while my friends are together after classes without me. The reality is that I wouldn't physically or mentally be able to keep up with a non-stop social life.

Bob and I go out together still and have a great time. We make adjustments, such as going to an earlier movie, so we don't get home late for me or choosing a restaurant closer to home, so I don't feel too far away. Bob loves to grill, and this has become a great option to dining out. During the past few years, he has become quite interested in different seasonings for chicken and meat and has become an expert in grilled salmon. I enjoy watching him have so much fun taking the lead with dinner. Needless to say, this has helped with our nightly debates of "What do you want for dinner?"

Bob and I have a pattern at the end of his workday. When preparing to leave the office, he texts or calls me to let me know he's on his way home. I always take a deep breath when he walks through the front door after work. He gives me hope when he comes home to give me a hug and kiss hello. During dinner, we sometimes watch reruns of Modern Family, Seinfeld, The Big Bang Theory or Everybody Loves Raymond.

These comedies provide a good laugh for a tough day. Throughout the evening, we recap the day's events and talk about trending topics on Twitter or the local news while we settle in to watch our favorite weekly TV shows—Chicago PD, Chicago Fire, and Billions. As always, Bob is patient with me when I can't keep track of what channel each show is on at what time.

Taking a step back from everything in life that moves so quickly and enjoying time with Bob, friends and family is what is important to me now. We don't get unlimited chances in life. I finally figured out that I'm still alive to make this mission real.

It's what I can do to hopefully reach one person and bring this topic a little more forward. Ever since the TBI, I make a point of creating memories and cherishing moments. I buy a T-shirt at every concert I attend, a Christmas ornament on each vacation, and a mug from every musical or play I attend. I write the date on the bottom and keep adding to the collections.

One of the most prevalent feelings I've had since waking up from the coma in 2008 is uselessness. I don't know if I am trying to talk myself out of feeling that way, or if I notice it on my bad days, but I feel it too often. When I tell people my story, a common response is, "You are so lucky to be alive. You should be thankful," or, "That should make you realize not to take life for granted." These are true statements with which I agree, but also ones that carry a lot of weight and responsibility.

Constantly acknowledging the defeat that non-survivors can never understand is so lonely that it's deafening. That is the moment when the noise stops and there is no escape. The doctors don't test for this emotion. There is not a hospital center to scan for these deficits; the ones that keep TBI survivors human. I guess we figure this part out and deal with it ourselves.

We don't have to do it alone, that's why our support system is so important. I get to tell someone at the end of the day that I survived the bad day. TBI survivors face the challenge of trying to survive without being able to do it alone. This is why we need support throughout the entire process.

Friends know that I'll need to go home early, but I still want to be part of the community while I am there. I don't want to be forgotten.

The tough thing about these situations is that I don't have the power to choose to be excluded. I just have to accept it. For a TBI survivor, that is much easier said than done. Those feelings of hypersensitivity and fear of isolation kick in. When friends don't invite me someplace, I feel desperate and alone. I also internalize those feelings and blame myself for not being good enough anymore for anyone to want.

If someone meets me on a bad day, they might never meet me on a good day. I need to keep reminding people this is not the only experience in my adult life. I already need to introduce a person to someone who doesn't exist anymore and will never come back. I need a chance to introduce myself now, before this version is gone. The old me doesn't exist anymore.

She disappears more and more, slipping through my fingers; becoming a vacant shadow of the past. I know she will never come back. An internal conflict I struggle with is trying too hard to get her back or suddenly not accepting that she is gone.

There are times I feel stuck and in static mode; afraid of the uncertainty ahead. I feel a battle between finding my confidence that was such a character trait of mine and my father's, and cowering in a quiet voice so I don't upset anyone to the point that they abandon me.

I am trying so hard to live in a positive place and not allow myself to wander into the realm of negativity. While I write this, I am reliving everything since that first fall, good and bad, successes and failures. I didn't know how vulnerable I would feel. I am fighting to dredge up bits of memories that I don't want to ever think about but need to include here for this to be authentic. I survived more than once—so I am not finished. I need to get myself back and get back to myself. I know how much that matters and that I almost lost it twice. It might have taken a decade to figure that out, but it was worth it, and it's a step back to unearthing who I was before 2008.

Chapter 17
Lessons Learned

I've been fortunate to learn many lessons about life as a TBI survivor from doctors, support groups, and from talking with fellow survivors. Before anything else, what I see is the biggest step, and sometimes the hardest, is to start by accepting that the TBI happened and that living with a TBI will be a factor of life moving forward. Everyone will reach this acceptance at different points in time. Survivors and loved ones may accept the TBI at different times, which can be difficult for both sides, but is human.

This is a mysterious injury, and in support groups, I've learned that it's important to understand that a brain injury is not anyone's fault, and it does not mean one is weak. Living in denial that the brain injury exists makes it impossible to take any steps forward in healing. Survivors, caretakers, and loved ones need to work together starting with acceptance and love. Survivors need constant reassurance by their support team that they will be loved even though their lives are different.

After acknowledging and accepting the brain injury as part of life, I learned that another important step on the road to recovery is to build your body and mind back up slowly. I never needed to know anything about brain injuries, seizures, neurologists, or any of the other effects from a TBI before. The most powerful way I gathered information was by asking questions. I asked all of my doctors—primary care, neurologist, psychiatrist—what a TBI was and what it would mean for Bob and me personally. I still don't ingest any medication without the doctor explaining what it is, what it will do, and if it will interact with others I currently take.

Bob and my mom diligently asked questions each time they saw anyone in a white coat or pair of scrubs walk down the hall to my room. Eventually, they all started to run down the hall because they knew an onslaught of questions was coming their way.

This isn't a battle to let someone else fight. I also asked ways that my doctors recommended for me to best empower myself to get stronger. My case is not entirely up to them—if there is anything I can do to help myself, I want to work at it. We always want to know what the most credible and relevant resources are that we can learn from as a family. In the beginning, it's important to take these steps slowly because the body is still healing from the trauma, but every little bit of knowledge helps chip away at the unknown.

It took about a month before I was strong enough to walk around my own condo, and then outside around the condo walkways. Of course, I needed Bob's assistance to help myself up and walk in any type of straight line. It was a great victory to take those first few steps outside and succeed. These three-minute walks turned into five-minute walks, and then ten-minute walks. Bob kept telling me how proud he was of me. After slowly building up to taking walks by myself, I joined the YMCA next door and began to workout. Getting stronger physically and learning more about my condition really helped me believe that I could live in a world with possibilities.

The body is amazing in its capacity to heal. It will also tell us when it needs more time. I definitely jumped out of the gate too soon at times, pushed myself too hard some days, and so I had setbacks. That became, and still is, a part of how I live with my TBI. I'm not reckless, but there are days that I want to go to a U-Jam Fitness® or Zumba® event to be with my friends. The energy we share drains me, but it's worth experiencing the happy, celebrating lift it provides. I don't mind staying in bed for the following two days to recuperate. The reason I volunteer to teach Zumba® is for my students. I play the songs they request. I practice like crazy for class and fine tune the order of songs in the playlist until minutes before class. I'll spend about an hour each day practicing for the one-hour class, and two hours the day of class. I want to give them one hour that is just for them.

Trying to find the right consistency for me is a work in progress. My new normal is also a space in which I've taken a close look at limits. As I cycle through increasing my strength and stamina, and fighting through more falls and health complications, I'm learning what my limits are and how hard I can push physically and mentally. Some of these I deal with are often based on peoples' preconceived assumptions that I shouldn't physically be attempting something; like walking down the street or to have lunch with a friend. This is a great opportunity for me to thank people for caring about me and also raising a little education about my condition.

Once I gained my strength and learned to live with a TBI, I wanted to find ways that I could help make a difference in spreading TBI education and awareness. My friends told me there was such a need for me to get involved with advocacy because they didn't know enough about my condition after being friends with me for ten years.

Those conversations opened my eyes that I could be effective on a local level, or at least I would try. Volunteering with local brain injury advocacy and support groups has also been incredibly healing for me.

Talking with other survivors, or sharing my story to groups of people, brings back a little piece of me as a person and makes this journey more personal and less clinical. That gives a glimmer of hope that there is more ahead for me and how I can be a voice in my community.

I love leading a group, being on stage, or being part of something to grow community. It is not about the spotlight being on me or people watching me. When I am on stage as part of an event, whether it is training or fundraising, I have the honor to engage with the crowd because I am there for them.

Leading is about guiding, inspiring, and raising awareness about something, offering a variety of options to open the mind, trying something new out of my comfort zone and letting those feelings and ideas grow among the crowd. I don't have any butterflies or stage fright. That fear went away in college when I took on a lot of leadership roles outside of the classroom.

I was the yearbook editor, wrote for the school newspaper, was part of student government, and led a lot of peer education groups and retreats at school.

In the past, I made presentations and spoke at various meetings and in front of different groups of which I was a member. I always prepared meticulously. If someone gave me the generosity of their time, I never took it for granted. I showed up one hundred percent. One of the goals I hope will come from this book is being able to speak at schools about brain injury awareness. I can't wait to be in front of students again. I am aching to teach again, to lead a discussion from the heart to spark questions and dialogue among people.

Chapter 18
Call to Action for TBI Conversations

The question I ask myself so frequently is, "How do we increase brain injury education, so people will stop with the hurtful conversations?" I'm a member of the traumatic brain injury world and I welcome anyone to ask me questions and open a discussion about it so our brave voices can spread awareness together. Three-minute conversations can turn into five-minutes. Weekly check-ins with a few people can grow to serve much wider audiences.

The responsibility can start with survivors and their loved ones. The first level of responsibility falls on our shoulders to share our stories, when ready, and truly allow people to understand what this disability is, how we live our lives and why we are so passionate about paving the way forward.

Most importantly, it is on the shoulders of survivors to work with foundations, schools of all grade levels, organized sports, sporting goods companies, hospital inpatient rehab programs, parent associations, gyms and athletic clubs, doctors, hospitals, the media, and more. We need to break down our walls, reach across to support each other, and lay the foundation for the next brave voices to speak louder.

To date, the entertainment industry, which reaches and influences so many people, does not help open the door to true education, representation, and dialogue and the realities of brain injuries. It's 2018 and actors are using head trauma as fodder for comedy. This insensitivity is not acceptable and does not set a good example to laugh at people with brain injuries.

I want to start an open dialogue about what it means to live with a TBI. But strength does not grow from separation and hiding, it grows from acceptance.

Where are the brave voices who will speak with TBI survivors in public? As of today, brain injury doesn't have a public icon for advocacy. This might be the exact reason for the lack of awareness throughout our communities, but that is wherein the challenge lies.

This topic is not taboo, it is not going away, and it is getting bigger every day. In the United States, every twenty-three seconds someone suffers a brain injury, ultimately affecting more than 2 million individuals annually. TBI costs the United States more than $56 billion a year. More than 5 million Americans alive today have had a TBI resulting in a permanent need for help in performing daily activities.

Survivors of TBI are often left with significant cognitive, behavioral, and communicative disabilities, and some patients develop long-term medical complications, such as epilepsy, Parkinson's disease, and Alzheimer's disease.[17] We need to get the facts out, dispel the myths, and stop the jokes about brain injury. At least that can be a start.

Survivors need to feel welcome and safe to share their stories if and when they are ready. For me, it took some time before I was comfortable, confident, and educated enough about what a TBI is to tell people about it. As someone who survived a trauma, sharing that experience is not just telling a story, it's opening up my soul to someone and letting them in through my most vulnerable door; a door that I am afraid to open at times because it is so deep inside of me beyond the walls I have built up for self-preservation.

One of the many points I've learned in speaking to other survivors is that sharing our stories aloud can be very helpful in our healing process. We need to speak to friends, family members, and those closest in our lives, as well as strangers. A brain injury has the potential to reach anyone so we need to reach everyone. It's time to open this discussion publicly with artists, writers, freethinkers, thought leaders, teachers, and students.

We need to reach those who have empathy and those who need to learn empathy. Any one of us could become or be a TBI survivor, lose someone to a TBI, or care for someone with a TBI. More importantly, any of us could have walked away from someone with a TBI.

Brain injuries are so prevalent and not being addressed enough to show the breadth and severity of this pandemic. This is why we need to create a culture of human compassion, and then cultivate a paradigm of sympathy. So how do we do that? We need to put down the phones and talk to each other face to face. People tell me I'm brave to admit the details of what a TBI does to my life, the nightmares and flashbacks I have, the post-traumatic stress that hasn't gotten better, taking away my sense of purpose.

Medicine does not have a cure or treatment for brain injuries. Damaged brain cells do not regenerate, and there are still not enough resources devoted to brain injury research. People typically don't want to look someone with a brain injury in the eye because they feel uncomfortable around someone who is different.

Too often, the negative stereotypes of brain damage rush to mind before engaging in a conversation with someone living with the condition. Another reason people don't want to talk about a TBI is that it is something that can happen to them—to anyone.

Brain injuries are not reserved for athletes, alcoholics, genetic predispositions, men, women, or anyone who chooses to live a certain lifestyle. Everyone is fair game to this monster, which is scary, but it's not something you can 'catch.'

It's frustrating to feel as though your fight and advocacy fall on deaf ears. When this happened to me at first, I wanted to give up on all brain injury awareness and education. I felt like the world didn't care about what I wanted to say, about the story I needed to share and how any progress could happen. I was so discouraged, but had no idea how to stop crying, get up off my living room floor, and figure out a different way, because what I was doing wasn't working. I reached out to my mentors and role models at Zumba®, U-Jam Fitness® and the Project Athena Foundation, asking for advice.

Each of them offered similar guidance through a different lens and empowered me to keep working. I reached out to support groups, asking if I could attend a program to share my story and provide inspiration. I sought out groups, places, and institutions for how I could help and participate. I remember looking at my inbox over and over again, until the SDBIF responded, and I've been volunteering with them since.

Raising awareness about this issue is so important to me in a way that only survivors might understand. My worst days and lowest points are the times that I want to speak up the most, because I am in pain, which means another survivor is in pain.

I'm going to keep sharing my story and using my voice. Some people will listen and some people will walk away. It's not going to stop me because one day my voice will make a difference.

I still keep in contact with these mentors about my projects. They saved me when I was at the bottom and ready to give up completely. They lifted me off my living room floor, gave me hope to keep at it and guided me along the way. I am now a resource of education and advocacy for others affected by brain injuries. Giving up is not the answer and asking for help is always worth a shot.

It's not always easy to start talking about brain injuries, but there are some ways to make a smooth transition into the conversation and to help people new to the subject feel more comfortable. It's more productive to start a discussion about a topic which is often avoided by taking an engaging and constructive tone, with a level voice, rather than becoming defensive and yelling.

The goal of sharing our experiences is to raise education about the realities of brain injuries and what it means to live with a TBI. I am a functioning adult living with a TBI. There is no reason to fear me or move away from me. These are opportunities to show how a variety of brain injuries manifest and what they 'look like.' This is also the perfect time for survivors to share what types of physical and rehabilitative therapies are available and expand the conversation on that subject alone.

These are big subjects to handle, but important ones. When a survivor talks about what they have been through, it's a moment for listeners to become more educated about brain injuries and then act as vehicles to spread what they have learned.

It is amazing to listen to each other and gain an appreciation for what the details of life are like for a TBI survivor. Discussing brain injuries more informally might provide a forum for a survivor to share for the first time who hasn't found a comfortable setting yet. Each of these actions creates more results for others, and more after them. Our choices are important which is why sharing our stories has the potential to be very powerful on a global scale and can provide hope for people affected by TBIs.

I've had many conversations with others based on how movies can skew someone's interpretations of brain injuries. I've noticed that when people don't really know exactly how to carry on a conversation with me when learning that I have a TBI, they will immediately say, "Oh, I saw the movie, *Concussion (2015)*, so I understand exactly what you are going through." *Concussion* focuses on chronic traumatic encephalopathy (CTE), a degenerative brain disease caused by a history of repetitive brain trauma.[18]

The film documents research by pathologist Bennet Omalu of the first evidence of CTE in a football player and how CTE destroyed his life. Progression of CTE includes impulse control problems, aggression, depression, paranoia, memory loss, confusion, impaired judgment, and often, dementia.

I politely interject, "I saw that film too, but CTE isn't actually what my condition is." When I try to continue the conversation in hopes of raising TBI awareness with someone already engaged in the conversation, recipients turn their backs or just skip over it.

When I try to describe the times when I struggle with retention and feeling displaced, people often ask, "So is your life like living in the movie *50 First Dates (2004)*?" In the film, Drew Barrymore's character suffers from limited anterograde amnesia from a car accident years ago.

This condition is a temporary loss of the ability to store new memories as a result of brain injury, which is why she wakes up each day thinking she is living the same day over again.[19]

This question makes me uneasy because I feel similar at times, but I have a different condition. I often wonder why so many people recognize the brain trauma difficulties in this popular film. Is it because they enjoy the entertainment, or is it because they understand that the leading character lives with a brain injury? When I ask this question, nobody is able to articulate an answer; they give me a blank stare and move onto a different topic, despite my efforts to open a conversation. To ask someone with a brain injury such an intimate question, it's important to allow them the courtesy to take the time to answer.

These are just examples regarding brain injury. So many movies, shows, plays, and other forms of media have the potential to touch on vulnerabilities within each of us. While I used to think that was depicted to cause pain, the truth is that so much is about a lack of education. With this understanding and communication, I believe there is hope in joining our voices together in bravery.

Together, we can break the stigma about people with brain injuries. Living with a TBI is trying to survive in a world we cannot find. Living with a brain injury means fighting every day to start over, pleading for patience and not giving up.

Chapter 19
Growing Self-Confidence

One positive surprise that came out of this entire journey is that I finally developed some self-confidence. After each fall, I always stand up with a bit more assurance. It's ironic that I was always so self-conscious about the trivial things. I never felt like I was pretty enough or dressed well enough or was fun enough because I never fit in with the 'popular kids.' Now, I feel empowered because I am the 'different one.' I am not interested in being a nameless and faceless follower in a large group. I prefer to stand out for my authentic individuality and my original thoughts.

Pulling from my inner strength are the times that I feel confident commanding a room again, with purpose. I attend events with friends that bring me joy when I feel strong enough. When people talk down to me or laugh at me for not having the energy to stay out all night, I choose to hold my head up. There are times when I get overwhelmed socially and have too much anxiety, in which case I apologize. Someone who won't accept that apology or give another chance will always be known as the person who chose to walk away from a brain injury survivor reaching out for support. That behavior demonstrates their insecurities toward my strength, something for which I will not apologize, especially as an adult who is working to build grassroots TBI advocacy.

Trying to move forward and thrive in my new normal does not allow room for such toxic relationships and dynamics with people. I believe that for both sides. Maintaining a relationship with someone who doesn't want me in their life is not where I put my energy. I believe we can be more united, compassionate, and forgiving.

Bob and I have spent the last decade becoming self-educated experts in TBI care. With each new complication, fall, ER visit, hospital discharge, setback, and victory, I step into unchartered waters often without any map guiding the way. The challenge is not knowing what we need to know ahead of time. When I left the hospital in 2008, in a wheelchair barely able to walk, I did not receive any physical therapy because I was considered too healthy and not sick enough to warrant earning a need for it.

The hospital also did not discharge me with an occupational therapy plan. Instead, we made adjustments at home each time I encountered a task that used to be simple, like taking a shower or reaching for my clothes. Back then, we didn't have the time to learn about resources unknown to us. We were trying to manage my pain day by day and focus on helping me wake up in the morning.

Fast forward ten years and some days I wake up bright-eyed and filled with a little too much adrenaline, more than I'm ready for. The day of the photoshoot for the cover of this book was the most fascinating study in human behavior I'd ever experienced. It was a day of sliding doors. Each moment of the morning was glorious and held optimistic intention, and from the second my right foot touched the concrete curb back at home, the dark side of humanity flooded me with gut punches.

I woke up that morning feeling alive with purpose. I put on makeup, styling my hair to look nice for an afternoon out in the park. We didn't go anyplace exotic or extraordinary, just to the local park near my house. We didn't close off areas of the park or ask people to move away from where we wanted to take pictures; we walked around until we found open spots to take natural, candid photos. The best part of the day was spending time with close friend and talented, professional photographer, Karla Trujillo. We caught up and talked about the exciting plans each of us had. Then, we would pause, and she would take a series of photos when the light fell right or when the fountain sprayed the sunshine with water. I felt glamorous for that one day in the park, wearing a pair of jeans, makeup, and hairspray because I had so much energy and felt like a leader again. I was back in my old normal, at peace.

Then the sliding door opened and closed. When I got home after the photoshoot, I said hello to a man I see every day at my condo complex, went inside to change into comfortable workout clothes, and take off the heavy makeup I wore specifically for the camera. I pulled my hair into a ponytail and took Emmie outside for a walk ten minutes later, where I saw the same man again.

I said 'Hi, it's good to see you again."

He looked at me with a perplexed glance and asked, "Oh, are you walking Megan's dog for her?"

"What do you mean?" I asked. "This is my dog, you see me with her all the time."

He was still confused. "No, I saw Megan outside."

"Yes, I'm Megan. I just changed my clothes and took off my makeup."

"Really? I recognize your voice," he questioned. "But outside was Megan looking beautiful."

Then he turned and pointed at me.

He waved his hand in the air, motioned up and down the silhouette of my body and said, "I see this every day."

I actually had no words with which to respond. I just said, "See you tomorrow," and walked inside with dignity, even though my heart ached a little for being judged and dismissed based on my outward appearance.

Ten minutes before this interaction, I felt so strong and excited about the next steps to come, and here I was presented with a choice to let this man take away my power or not. When I was in my house, my comfort zone, I allowed myself to take the ten minutes of crying that I needed so I could move forward.

I stood up, took a few deep breaths and decided that he and his judgment would not win, because nobody else gets to define me. He doesn't know anything about my life or my brain injury. The truth is that I do wear my workout clothes most days because they are comfortable around the house and to wear while sitting and writing this book and doing other online volunteer work for nonprofit brain injury awareness groups, which I do with pride and honor. I don't wear makeup or style my hair for this type of day either. I work hard on every project I pick up that has my name on it.

While I left that ignorant conversation outside, there was one small part that creeped into my home. The one place I had kept free from the lab reports, MRIs, CTs, charts, and test results that defined me as a patient was my home. With one swift breath, I could have been anyone, just like I am in the hospital. I couldn't process that a man would look a woman in the eye and call her 'this' without realizing the effect it could have. That day, one man used one word that violated my safe space at home where I had felt like a person. Rather, he tried to violate my safe space, but did not breach the front doors. I had grown in self-confidence during the last decade that impersonal and dehumanizing comments, whether related to a TBI or not, were not going to define me.

Chapter 20
Finding Identity and Gaining Purpose

I am constantly searching for my lost identity because I don't have all of myself and I feel incomplete at times. I don't always know how or where I fit in, which has been an issue amplified with the social anxiety from the TBI. I won't solidify my identity in only a medical context because there is more to me than numbers. Socially, to wear the label 'brain injury survivor' is defeating because there is not a place for us to fit in—except with each other. It's time for society to create a category for TBI survivors the same way other disabilities are acknowledged and safely accommodated for by legal standards. Based on conversations with other resilient TBI survivors I know, we are not giving up on ourselves anytime soon or on this standoff until our voices are heard.

It's not just those affected by brain injuries who are searching for themselves or trying to understand who they want to be. It is overwhelming to find a place where we belong while so many parts of life keep changing—work, family, love, finances, death, friends, illness, finances, children, and more.

Some of these we choose to discuss and some not. Aspects of each, start to define us. This is a first step to building who we are step by step. Now I found a way to fit in even though I need to do things at my pace.

In March 2018, I wanted to find a way to raise TBI awareness, especially since March is Brain Injury Awareness Month. Living in a current culture that revolves around social media, I decided to share either an educational or inspirational post about brain injury survivors each day on Facebook, Instagram, and Twitter.

My posts stayed quiet for the first three days, with a handful of friends 'liking' them, but not commenting. The fourth post, in which I stated that, "I'm a Proud Traumatic Brain Injury Warrior," got some attention. People I knew from all areas of my life commented on that post for three days and sixty-five people 'liked' it on Facebook and twenty-six on Instagram. That was the most activity these posts had seen to date.

Other brain injury survivors and support groups from around the world reached out to me as a resource, which is when everything came together. Before I realized it, I'd carved my way back to my role as a teacher. Slowly, more people are starting to engage communication about brain injury on social media. I also became extremely focused on writing this book at the time. I've discovered TBI advocacy and awareness is a great way to continue my role as an educator.

This is the first time in ten years that I am finding a sense of purpose. With excitement for diving into the dream of teaching again while increasing awareness of TBI also came fear. The same fear that creeps up when trying anything new, that of not meeting expectations. I set expectations for myself, but higher ones for my family, friends, publisher, volunteer groups, and most of all, readers and TBI survivors. I knew that the correct way to write this book was through a lens of respect and honor for other brain injury survivors, bringing justice and awareness to the topic while breaking the stigma of brain injury.

One of my dreams has always been to write a book. This is not the subject that I planned, but that isn't what matters. The bigger picture is that I am working hard to achieve my dream. I reached out for support, guidance, and education, and I learned every step of the way. There were other times in my life that I tried to write a book, but I never wrote very much. I am finally confident that I have something to say and share with the world.

Writing this book has been a journey like no other for me, as I encountered hurdles from the start that never occurred to me. Long-term effects of the TBI in 2008 are still not resolved.

My cognition, focus, energy, and concentration are at the weakest point in years.

I started to write this book just three months after I fell and broke my face in September 2017, while still healing from that accident. The most surprising element was that I would sit down to process this whole trauma at one time and merge all components of the past decade together.

The impact of this extreme overflow of emotion is forcing me to dig to the low points around which I've built walls to keep me from returning. I don't cower away if I face someone who doesn't have the strength to look me in the eye. It might have taken ten years to figure that out, but it was worth it, and it's a step back to unearthing who I was before 2008. When I put all of this together, including analyzing the process, it has been incredibly healing for me as a TBI survivor.

Establishing a purpose again to do something meaningful with my life has felt like a challenge since July 2008, when control of so many choices to come slipped through my fingers. This void has felt the emptiest for me. This is the longest stretch of time I have not had a job, the most often that my health has been so poor and I've felt so much pain, the period I've worried about money so much that it brings me to tears, the first time I've struggled with my learning comprehension taking a serious setback, and the most helpless I've been without my own independence.

These situations are not unique to me, which is why I never gave up—I knew I was never alone. There has always been someone to lift me out of these low trenches and inspire me to get out of bed the next day, because the hard times do turn around. Sometimes it's Bob, someone else in the family, or a friend who gives me the boost I need, and sometimes it can be a stranger who stops to ask if I'm all right or smiles at me, which in turn, inspires me to reach out to someone I see in pain.

Chapter 21
What's Next?

Why do I say that I refuse to let the TBI define me? Because there is so much more to me than an accident in 2008. My friends and family sometimes forget what I did and who I was before the accident. I need to remind them of what filled my life before I was twenty-nine years old, which makes me sad. The people who I've only met since the 2008 TBI don't know anything about an entire life I led that made me who I am now—the person and not just the patient.

I also want more for myself than to be defined as just the girl with the TBI. It took some time to adjust, because at first, the TBI was all I knew since my old world was gone and I was bedridden for my first month home. Then I put all of my energy into learning about my TBI and getting stronger. The more I built up, the more I was able to create multiple dimensions of my life in my new normal. I think if I allow the TBI to define me, that I will live too much in the past, and not take new chances. That is the last way I want to live.

Another concern I have about making the choice to let my TBI define me is that I isolate myself. My support team has been incredible to me, and I never want anyone to feel like I would ever take advantage of their generosity and kindness.

However, I can't wait for the day that these relationships are not based on taking care of me as the sick person. I'm determined to find my identity or create one to thrive in my new normal. I want to be a three-dimensional person and not just a patient.

It's hard to strike that equilibrium when I wear a medical bracelet every day with my name, date of birth, condition (TBI/SEIZURE) and allergy to penicillin. The information on that bracelet both saves my life and diminishes it at the same time. It's such a hideous dull stainless-steel chain with the universal red symbol for medical alert. People look at it on my wrist and then look up at me curiously. I don't want to shroud it among other jewelry since the purpose of it is to stand out for paramedics to see in case of an emergency.

As much as I dislike the bracelet, I'm not taking if off. It turns out that it really is part of my identity and my safety. That bracelet is the only stable certainty of my new normal. It doesn't change. It is in the same place and looks the same every moment of every day.

I can't say that for much else, at least not yet. I can't schedule my weeks or days specifically, which was a big part of the 'old me.' I came to terms with that loss a very long time ago.

Instead of focusing on overscheduling myself, I stop to appreciate that I am alive. I have deficits and I fight through them, because I appreciate everything more now than ever. I'm a proud, resourceful, and confident fighter. I push through for myself, my husband, my family and friends, and my doctors who keep supporting me and believing in me. I make the choice to stand stronger so other survivors see that hope can survive even during the tough days.

I take advantage of the flexibility in my schedule that allows me the opportunity to be part of something bigger than just me. This drives me to keep going. Getting up after falling or being pushed is hard. Standing up with strength and integrity is courageous and heroic. Those are the shoes in which I want to walk and create a community to foster. I believe there are endless possibilities. I need to remember how strong I am and how much my body wants to keep fighting.

I am finding my identity in an empowered way and awakening a new side of me. A part of me will never give up being a teacher. I will find ways to spark thought-provoking conversations and encourage people on their journey to learn more about themselves, which is why I started teaching.

The other certainty I know is that there is more ahead for me. When I left the hospital in 2008, the doctors thought I wouldn't walk again. My response was to become a dance fitness instructor licensed in six specialties. I'm grateful for dance fitness coming into my life when it did for so many reasons. One of the beautiful benefits I discovered is the therapeutic and healing power of music. When people ask me how I am able to function during the overwhelming times, I tell them the first thing I do is put my earbuds in and listen to my 'mindful breathing' playlist. I tune out all of the outside noise and chaos, and I own my space for those moments.

What of my old life exists? Is there any part of it that I want back? Teaching feels like home. Maybe it's because of the ways the teachers in my life influenced me. It's the job where I worked the hardest. I never took that job for granted and never truly let go.

I feel like these past ten years I've been sitting in the waiting room, not knowing what the next chapter of my life holds while I wait for permission to write my story. What am I waiting for? Ten years is long enough. This is now my time to stand up and leave those uncomfortable plastic chairs in the impersonal room behind. I'm confident to walk out of those hospital doors and into the world. I am ready to handle whatever tests, results, medications, and unknowns come my way. I've earned confidence sitting in that room.

One goal of my testimony is to reach the family members and friends of TBI survivors; those who become the caregivers. It's impossible to truly understand what each aspect of life is like for a TBI survivor, especially since it is often harder than ever for survivors to communicate specifics to other people. Anything that can share a glimpse first-hand from a survivor might offer insight to a caregiver for a loved one.

I will not be a silent survivor. This book isn't only for me. Those blank days gave me a restart button to take chances and explore new opportunities for which I felt too small before. I found the courage to be and use my strong voice in my new normal. My journey is mine to tell without needing permission from anyone.

I am back commanding a room and being the one who has something to say. I'm looking at the world through healed eyes. My dreams have changed, so I changed the route to my dreams.

I want to inspire others—even one person, not being limited to the TBI community. I am not the only person who, at some point in life, has tried to find hope in a time of despair. These ten years mean something. We do not have just one moment that defines our entire life or tells our whole story. Every moment matters and everything we do is important. Sharing my experience and this journey is to be a service for others beyond those who live through tragedies. We all face choices every day and each of us has one hundred percent power over the choices we make. I own my choices with pride.

There are countless times I could have chosen to give up on this journey. Instead, I chose hope, and I will continue to do so, discovering new parts of myself, dancing with confidence and facing the world head-first in my new normal.

We are not alone in this world. Each of us is looking to make a connection. We hold our open hands and hearts out as human beings without judgment. That is how a community can develop with a foundation of optimism and hope, as hope survives.

Endnotes

[1] "BIAA Adopts New TBI Definition," Brain Injury Association of America, accessed February 3, 2018.
https://www.biausa.org/public-affairs/public-awareness/news/biaa-adopts-new-tbi-definition.

[2] "Grand mal seizure-Overview," Mayo Clinic, accessed February 5, 2018.
https://www.mayoclinic.org/diseases-conditions/grand-mal-seizure/symptoms-causes/syc-20363458.

[3] "Status epilepticus," U.S. National Library of Medicine, accessed February 7, 2018.
https://www.ncbi.nlm.nih.gov/pmc/articles/PMC2824929/.

[4] "About Brain Injury Assessments in the Hospital - Glasgow Coma Scale," Brain Injury Association of America, accessed February 3, 2018.
https://www.biausa.org/brain-injury/about-brain-injury/diagnosis/assessments-in-the-hospital/glasgow-coma-scale.

[5] "Prehospital Use of Cervical Collars in Trauma Patients: A Critical Review," U.S. National Library of Medicine, accessed April 27, 2018.
https://www.ncbi.nlm.nih.gov/pmc/articles/PMC3949434/.

[6] "Traumatic Brain Injury-Symptoms & Causes," Mayo Clinic, accessed February 7, 2018.
https://www.mayoclinic.org/diseases-conditions/traumatic-brain-injury/symptoms-causes/syc-20378557.

[7] "DVT Prevention: Intermittent Pneumatic Compression Devices," Johns Hopkins Medicine, accessed February 22, 2018.
https://www.hopkinsmedicine.org/healthlibrary/test_procedures/cardiovascular/dvt_prevention_intermittent_pneumatic_compression_devices_135,328.

[8] "Ataxia-Overview," Mayo Clinic, accessed February 7, 2018.
https://www.mayoclinic.org/diseases-conditions/ataxia/symptoms-causes/syc-20355652.

[9] "Grand mal seizure-Overview," Mayo Clinic, accessed February 5, 2018. https://www.mayoclinic.org/diseases-conditions/grand-mal-seizure/symptoms-causes/syc-20363458.

[10] "Seizures-Overview," Mayo Clinic, accessed February 5, 2018. https://www.mayoclinic.org/diseases-conditions/seizure/symptoms-causes/syc-20365711.

[11] "Traumatic Brain Injury-Symptoms & Causes," Mayo Clinic, accessed February 7, 2018. https://www.mayoclinic.org/diseases-conditions/traumatic-brain-injury/symptoms-causes/syc-20378557.

[12] "I'm Going Home": Discharges Against Medical Advice," National Center for Biotechnology Information, U.S. National Library of Medicine, accessed February 7, 2018. https://www.ncbi.nlm.nih.gov/pmc/articles/PMC2664598/.

[13] "Hypothyroidism (underactive thyroid)," Mayo Clinic, accessed February 16, 2018. https://www.mayoclinic.org/diseases-conditions/hypothyroidism/symptoms-causes/syc-20350284.

[14] "Endocrine failure after traumatic brain injury in adults," National Center for Biotechnology Information, U.S. National Library of Medicine, accessed February 14, 2018. https://www.ncbi.nlm.nih.gov/pubmed/16960299/.

[15] "Trying to Recover From A TBI? What Reading, Stress & Exercise All Have In Common During the Healing Process," Plasticity Brain Centers, accessed February 16, 2018. https://www.plasticitybraincenters.com/media/trying-recover-tbi-reading-stress-exercise-common-healing-process/.

[16] "Trying to Recover From A TBI? What Reading, Stress & Exercise All Have In Common During the Healing Process," Plasticity Brain Centers, accessed February 16, 2018. https://www.plasticitybraincenters.com/media/trying-recover-tbi-reading-stress-exercise-common-healing-process/.

[17] "About SDBIF-Mission & Vision," San Diego Brain Injury Foundation, accessed February 7, 2018.
https://sdbif.org/about-sdbif/.

[18] "WHAT IS CTE?" Concussion Legacy Foundation, accessed May 2, 2018.
https://concussionfoundation.org/CTE-resources/what-is-CTE.

[19] "Could Drew Barrymore's memory loss in 50 First Dates really happen?" The Register, accessed March 2, 2018.
http://www.theregister.co.uk/2006/05/06/the_odd_body_amnesia/.

I never thought of you as Brain
Damaged / physically impaired.

A little "quirky" maybe.

Yet tired easy, But Nothing serious

until you told me about your "accident"/seizure.